D1450528

The Culprit

MARTIN SASEK

COPYRIGHT

The events and conversations in this book have been set down to the best of the author's ability, although some names and details have been changed to protect the privacy of individuals. This is a creative work of nonfiction. Some parts have been altered in varying degrees, for various purposes.

The Culprit Copyright © 2020 by Martin Sasek.

All Rights Reserved. No part of this book may be reproduced or used in any manner without written permission of the copyright owner except for the use of quotations in book review. For more information: TheCulprit.ca@gmail.com

First paperback edition May 2020
Cover Illustration Copyright © 2020 Martin Sasek Cover Design by SV can Design
Edited by Martin Sasek
Book Formatting by: Ardent Artist Books

ISBN: 978-1-7771805-0-8 (Paperback book)
ISBN: 978-1-7771805-1-5 (Electronic book)
ISBN: 978-1-7771805-2-2 (Hardcover book)
ISBN: 978-1-7771805-3-9 (Audio Book)
978-1-7771805-6-0 Die Culprit (German Edition) Hardcover
978-1-7771805-5-3 Die Culprit (German Edition) Ebook
978-1-7771805-4-6 Die Culprit (German Edition) Paperback

www.TheCulprit.ca

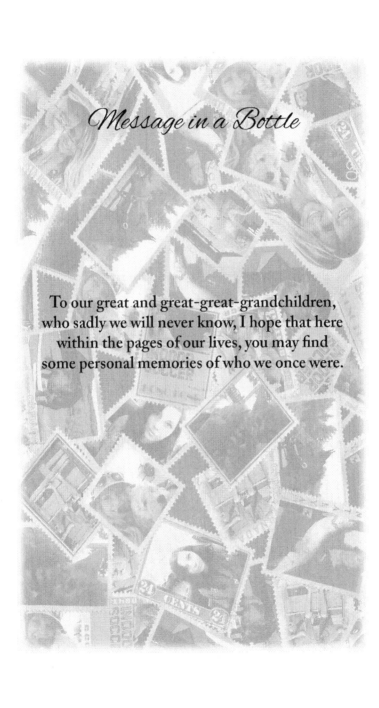

Message in a Bottle

To our great and great-great-grandchildren,
who sadly we will never know, I hope that here
within the pages of our lives, you may find
some personal memories of who we once were.

For Zahra.

And for Diane.
For her unwavering love and support.

TABLE OF CONTENTS

PREFACE

When I was working on my undergraduate studies at the University of Guelph, a compulsory read for a Canadian history course that I was taking was a book called Ten Lost Years—a collection of anecdotal stories from people who survived through the difficult years of the Great Depression.

So much so did I enjoy reading the accounts of their trying times, I felt compelled one day to share my thoughts and opinions with the professor of the program.

After introducing myself and my appreciations to him, he surprisingly stunned me by casually proclaiming, "You know Martin, memories are fickle, so you have to take what you read with a grain of salt." Bewildered, I thought to myself, why would this man choose a book he considered half loaded with bunk, to better illustrate to his students the particulars of such an important chapter in human history?

Out of respect for him, or perhaps more likely out of fear of tainting my grade, I simply thanked him for his input on the matter and then dumbfoundedly stumbled and spilled out of his office and onto the campus grounds to further ponder his point.

Biting into a cream cheese bagel on a bench below a grand old maple, I quickly concluded that: Surely what makes a good true story so good, is the reader's realization that the good true story is actually, well, *true!*

And so to that, and on that day, I promised myself that should I ever have the opportunity to document any part of my own life experiences, I would commit to accurately and truthfully recollecting and retelling the facts as best as I possibly could.

That being said, except for a name changed to protect the not so innocent and a tweak of time and event for this novel's purpose, I have toiled to ensure that the words on the pages that follow hereafter are indeed a true story!

Empty Nested

After twenty-seven years of marriage Diane and I had finally graduated, earning and acquiring our combined degree with all the rights and privileges awarded to those now holding the official and distinguished title of *Empty Nester*!

And although my dear spouse required a moment to adequately accommodate this newly found freedom, I on the other hand, took to empty-nesting like a duck to water. For me, it was as if we were newlyweds again. We could come and go as we pleased, eat when and whatever we wanted, prance about the house half-naked or even stay up to all hours of the night wildly drinking and indulgently making love to our hearts' content.

Although and admittedly to the latter we never did, still just knowing that we could infused into our marriage a welcomed, albeit long-forgotten, sense of irresponsibility. But moreover, it was that once again we had each other's full and undivided attention—unshackled, as I often joked that we were, from the daily and seemly endless grind of parental duties and obligations.

Don't get me wrong, we loved our three children dearly and were sincerely proud of their personal and professional achievements. We'd regularly enjoy taking turns listening to endless ramblings about their contorted lives and all the mayhem that comes with adulthood—which served well not only to keep us in touch—but helped foster our ever-growing belief in the wisdom of moderate and prescheduled visitations.

Anyway, given that we didn't genuinely want for company, especially as we ran our own business from home and thereby spent most days together, we had to admit that the house often seemed a little quiet and so now and again the thought occurred to us that perhaps a little creature bashing about the place might add an element of cozy to our otherwise benevolent condition.

And why not? Many other middle-aged couples in our circle of friends and acquaintances were clearly benefitting emotionally from companionship with their animals. In fact, once we began to think about it, it became curiously apparent that most people spoke of the silly antics and the love they held for their pets more often than they did about their very own children!

After much discussion on the matter, and thoroughly appreciating from experience the responsibilities that come with pet ownership, we eventually agreed to give it a go. Soon after that, conversations around the dinner table revolved entirely around what kind of pet would best suit us.

A dog, given our impulsive natures to drop everything on a whim and fly out the door for hours or days at a time, we quickly realized would be impractical and unfair to the animal. A cat on the other hand seemed like a decision more in tune with our combined personalities and lifestyle. Certainly well able to entertain and care for themselves, mind their business without training or having to go out for regular walks, playful but not too bothersome, occasionally affectionate, and as an added gratuity, genetically encoded with an inherent need to protect us from unwanted vermin, seemed a made-to-measure solution, or a no-brainer, right?

That being said and agreed upon, if I had at that point deluded myself into believing that acquiring a kitten would be as easy and straightforward as trotting down to our local pet store and adopting the cutest of the bunch, I would have been sorely mistaken. Of this I could have little doubts, as I knew all too well that my Diane was of the kind that quickly took offence to the thought of being considered *the norm*—and also of whom it might be said, relished nothing better than the idea of manifesting her own destiny.

It went without saying however that her strength of character and self-determinism was for me, a big part of the attraction. In our marriage I'd always been the dreamer —inspiring a direction and setting a course for us—but once the sails had been firmly fixed and trimmed, it was she who in every way steered the ship that somehow always managed to get us there.

For Diane, it mattered little if the task at hand was as

simple as trimming a tree or as daunting and demanding as managing our business—anything less than going above and beyond the call of duty was, for her, simply not part of the equation. And if I had any misgivings about this, I'd have soon been decisively corrected, as only a few days after that I found myself the unexpected recipient of an impromptu briefing on the very matter of kitten and cat now looming up before us.

Early one morning, just before heading out to dress up her hair, she'd promptly parked herself at my bedside, and post-peck on my cheek, began to delineate the details of my duties before her eventual return only a few hours later.

"I'm leaving you with these photo-cards I printed off. Each has a picture of the particular breed we are considering, the name and a brief description on the back, see?" Flipping over back and forth a card to illustrate and demonstrate her point while effectively revealing her obviously low opinion of my intelligence.

"And here is a pen so that you can fill out this comment form that corresponds to each card, so that we can discuss your opinions over lunch," another peck, "when I get home."

Ever the dutiful husband and surely not wanting to diminish her enthusiasm, I eased up against the back of the headboard and began rifling through the stack of portraits that I would later describe as little more than an appallingly awful collection of *horrific circus freaks!*

. . .

THE HIGHLIGHTS of which went something like this:

1. *Scottish Fold* – a breed of domestic cat with a natural dominant gene mutation that affects cartilage throughout the body, causing the ears to "fold over."

Seriously? A cat with no ears, how am I supposed to talk to it? Definitely – No!

2. *Oriental Short Hair* – Orientals have almond-shaped eyes, a triangular head shape, large ears, and an elongated, slender, and muscular body.

Ugh!!! Looks like a rat –or wingless bat, I thought we were getting a cat?

3. *Donskoy* – also known as Don Sphynx or Russian Hairless, is a hairless cat breed of Russian origin.

OMG, Hun! It has no fur, how the hell am I supposed to pat a cat with no fur? Really? Why would anyone want furless cat?

4. *Munchkin Cat* – The Munchkin cat or Sausage cat is a newer breed of cat characterized by its very short legs, which are caused by a natural genetic mutation.

Wiener Dog! I.D.K – Maybe, Kinda

5. *Serval Cat* - are wild African felines that stand 54–62 cm (21– 24 in) at the shoulder and can weigh 9–18 kg (20–40 lb).

40 lbs? That's a fricking Cheetah! By the way, I looked up the price. $7500 is not in our cat-budget! Nice try!

6. Bengal Cat – Despite their wild appearance, Bengal cats are actually quite affectionate with their human families. They also have high energy and a have interesting personalities.

Awesome! Love the markings. This is good! P.S. - What does it mean exactly by interesting personalities?

AND DESPITE BEING TYPICALLY and perhaps self-admittedly somewhat less socially savvy than our clever counterparts, even a husband can sometimes recognize when he has been manically maneuvered into a position of approval. Still, no worse for wear, I had to admit she'd chosen well and almost immediately after that the two of us became quite excited at the prospect of prospecting for Bengals.

Well, it wasn't long before Diane, armed with a shortlist of potential breeders in hand, had crafted and created a beautifully colour-coded map of the various *catteries* triangulated in and between Toronto, Windsor and the golden shores of Georgian Bay. Each pin marked with a photo and brief description of the kittens available there for adoption.

Realizing the considerable amount of geography that now lay ahead of us, I felt fortunate at having had the interest and ambition, some years earlier, to acquire a Private Pilot's License. Subsequently then managing the ownership of an elderly but well restored Cessna, that would now allow us not only to consider a broader range of possibilities but make planning weekend missions to some moggy destination all the more fun and exciting.

And so, by late November—just as us poor Canadians were once again embattled in the inclement hell that is the North— we found kitten hunting to be a warm and welcome diversion from the cold rains and bleak colourless landscapes that faith-fully sweep over Southern Ontario at that time of year.

What we couldn't have known then, however, but would soon come to discover, was that finding the right match for us was to be more complicated than we could have ever possibly imagined. More specifically, and much to our surprise, it would be less so the kittens themselves and more so their offbeat and peculiar humans that too often had us backpedaling for the doorway.

Not to say that cat breeders as a kind are a little off the grid or anything, but I'll tell you we met some really "interesting personalities" along the way. And if memory serves me well, it was stop number one that set the bar for all those that followed to be sure.

I remember it was an entirely still and overcast morning

that we'd lifted off from our home base at Edenvale. In the dense frigid air, we quickly and easily climbed to our cruise altitude, then banked right and set heading southwestward —our wingtips ever so gently scraping and scratching along the under-belly of the cloud cover.

After about an hour or so peacefully lofting high above the vast expanse of farms, rivers and towns that stretched seemingly beyond the horizon, we finally touched down on runway 27 at St. Thomas Airport, just across the Pond and not far up the way from Cleveland.

As soon as we had parked and chocked down the old kite, we rang for a cab and made our way into the small but quaint terminal building to expedite the *fifties-plus* involuntary expedition to the lavatory. By the time Diane had eventually engineered herself a cup of complimentary tea with two milk and two sweeteners, of course, the courteous receptionist alerted us that our taxi had arrived at the front door.

The driver, a rather jovial fellow and an apparent aviation enthusiast, who clearly preferred to discuss planes rather than cats, felt compelled to begin educating the two of us as to the notable aeronautical history of his family, beginning, but not ending with, his grandfather's impressive military service flying Spitfires for the RAF during World War Two. As he droned on my thoughts rather impolitely began to drift, as one tends to do however when they are filled with excitement and anticipation. After all, I'd never been to a breeder's operation, cat or otherwise, and curiosity was getting the better of me—so I began to imagine what it might look like.

In my mind's eye I envisioned a quintessential country farmhouse battened in a palish blue wooden siding with white trimmed accents. A column of rustic red brick charmingly circled the foundation, spilling out a stepstone pathway that meandered along to a set of rod iron gates quaintly perched at the roadside. And sitting, just gently, back from the house, a companion building attractively adorned with a wooden-carved sign that elegantly read *The Cattery*.

The walls inside the reception area were regally ornamented with pictures of royal feline ancestry, tastefully underlined with a pennant of certificates and awards. The breeder, fashionably styled in a coloured collar and elegantly embroidered logo of the operation, politely asked us to accompany her to the nursery.

The corridor to the viewing area was walled, floor to ceiling, with a large glass encasement that smartly showcased the parents of available kittens. At the center of the nursery room stood a tall aluminum pedestal supporting a large glass housing spattered and splashed with adorable kittens romping and rollicking inside.

"WELL, HERE WE ARE FOLKS," cranked out our cabbie, as he eased off the road and onto a stop at the top of a long rural laneway—smashing my fantasy like a falling wall of shattered glass and revealing behind a snapshot of reality that could only be described as a *post-apocalyptic war zone.*

"Are you sure this is the right place?" Diane nervously asked.

His eyes smiling back at us through the rear-view mirror, he confirmed, "*Cat Lady,* right?" Then he initiated a rather slothfully slow navigation down the washboard and potted drive at a pace leisurely enough to allow Diane and me the time to satisfactorily sample the flavours of what we were seeing.

The fields to each side were littered with an eclectic mix of refuse and debris, that included but were certainly not limited to, heaps of old and worn tires, rusting window and doorless vehicles, appliances of all sorts, toppled over swing sets, toilets and cans of gas. All being veraciously ravaged and consumed by acres of knee-high fescue. Then down further onto the end where beneath the branches of a witchy old oak sat a clapboard shanty, that required only a denim-clad barefooted old-timer strumming on a banjo to fulfill the entire place's *Deliverance* motif.

"Do you mind waiting?" I begged the driver.

But he insisted instead that he had yet another fare, but "Not to worry, I'll return shortly to pick you both back up."

Having little choice in the matter, I only asked that he wait a moment while I telephoned the breeder to confirm all was well. A minute later the three of us gazed intently as a hand from inside the front window slowly pulled back the makeshift drapery, a Harley Davidson flag brandishing a hell-bent for leather skeleton rider, donning a rebel bandana, a joint clenched in his teeth and revving plumes of smoke from a pair of exhaust pipes that spelled out his motto, *Ride Free or Die!*

"Yes, I see you, please come in," requested the voice on the other end of the line.

After ejecting us from the vehicle our cabman quickly sped off, leaving us hacking and hawking in the torrent of his dust. Then like a pair of mindless zombies we inched our way past piles of salvage and on to the tattered and tired front door.

"Hey, come on in," cordially greeting us was a slightly statured young woman sporting a coarsely cropped ruff of platinum blonde hair that curiously complemented the compliment of tattoos etched and engraved on her ankles and arms.

Stepping into what I presumed was the kitchen, as it harboured an old-style fridge and stove, we were immediately taken back by the overwhelmingly repugnant odour of the place -- that if you could bottle it like wine, it might well be labeled as *moldy moss and timber with a bold aroma of earthy barnyard and hints of diaper.* Little wonder, as the old run-down shed was absolutely feline-filled to the rafters with cats and kittens of all sorts and kinds.

At stage left, a large African Serval sitting perched atop a steeped stack of beer cases was busying itself by devouring a lump of, what looked like, sardines from inside a large aluminum salad bowl—hissing, grinding and gritting its teeth at us each time it went for another mouthful. Front and center, the plywood island was coated with strange-looking creatures that bore and boasted large saucer eyes, baseball mitts for paws and fur like the curls of Berber carpet. High above the planked cupboards, an accumulation of cats had gathered like decorative crockery, crying and complaining about something that seemed, at very least, important to them.

"Hi, I'm Joanne," interrupting our stare, "you guys are here for the Silver Bengal, right?" she sought to ask while pulling a pack of Camels out from the back pocket of her cut-offs. Then, after a deep drag and a hearty exhale, she apologized, "Hate to break it to you guys like this, but the truth is I got *punked*."

"Pardon me?" I politely responded, bemused by her slang.

"Buddy *punked* me on the Silver. Showed up this morning bitching like a bitch, whining he'd called it first. The way he was going on figured he'd shit himself if I didn't sell it to him! Sorry, I couldn't find your number, but hey, I got a dirty litter of Browns I could show ya."

"Uhm, ya, sure, ok." was the best Diane and I had to offer back.

"Bonus, mom's around here somewhere, hang on I'll be right back."

Dashing off for the doorway before stopping momentarily to turn back, and with a little chuckle, tossed at us, "Oh, just watch out for the flying cats!"

Squinting my brows back to my beloved, I somewhat nervously asked, "What the hell is a flying cat?"

Well, no sooner had the words left my lips than did I notice that one of the island-countered saucer creatures was intently glaring in my general direction. Wiggling its hind-end, like a golfer shuffling his feet before a critical putt, it then leaped like a salmon into the air, spanning nearly half the room, before landing, I kid you not, perfectly on to the top of my very head.

"Whoa," Diane exclaimed out loud, then with a casual cackle, confirmed to me, "I guess that's a flying cat!

Eventually, and quite carefully, we managed to dislodge its sharp little claws from the depths of my cranium. And as I bent over to put it down onto the floor, thereupon, my attention was now quickly drawn to the threshold of the kitchen, where standing there grinning from ear to ear, was of all things, a baby, a human baby. She had nearly white-blonde hair, brilliant blue eyes, and was enrobed in a sleeveless nightgown that stopped just short of her bare feet.

With a dangling milk bottle clenched between her two front teeth and arms stretched out straight forward, she began teetering and tottering, swaying, and see-sawing her way towards us, in every way an infant image of Frankenstein's baby. Giggling like a giddy goose, and without a spot of bother, she just kept on *Frankensteining* her way past Di and me as if we weren't even there.

After several *roundings* of the room, doing her dandiest to stomp on a scattering of kittens fleeing for their lives, her mother finally returned, complaining that, "I can't find her anywhere. But anyhow, the cubs are in here." Then bending down and withdrawing the oven's bottom drawer, she began to explain, "Mom had them in here, so I figured no point in disturbing them. Anyway, aren't they cute?" —handing one, less than carefully, to each of us.

Suddenly, as we stood considering the kittens, our attentions were quickly redirected to the large Serval—convulsing and contorting, choking and dry heaving so dreadfully as to cause an instinctive cautious and careful retreat, fearing as we were that at any moment, it was surely going to explode! Holding it together, it instead, eventually, and thankfully, managed to upchuck an immense, cringe-making, bile-soaked ball of half-digested fish that went splattering out onto the floor.

"Damn it," Joanne cried out, while sidestepping baby Frankenstein and rushing away to find a roll of paper towel.

As we stood amongst the chaos deliberating over the kittens, and while having to admit the cubs were adorable, after careful consideration, we felt that in our hearts we were still committed to finding a Silver. And upon her return we politely thanked Joanne, said we'd think some more about it, and then hastily made our way up to the roadside to await our driver's return.

As we stood there recounting and amusing ourselves over what had just transpired, and foolishly believing we'd seen it all, hardly could we have imagined that stop number two had a serving of kooky all of its own!

Bad Manors

A few days hence, once we had sufficiently picked up and dusted ourselves off, we made plans to see a litter of silver cubs near Waterloo. As luck would have it, the airport in neighbouring Kitchener, was not only close by to the breeder, but also close by to where our youngest daughter Karly lived—who graciously agreed to collect us from the airfield the following Saturday and accompany us along for the viewing.

Now, as any parent will surely attest to, that despite being born from a common gene pool, the personalities of siblings can be so diverse that it can often make a man sit up and take notice of just how suave and sociable the postman actually was. Our three were no exception to the rule.

Karly, a petite and attractive brunette with beautiful green eyes and an infectious smile, had to her parent's utter bewilderment, chosen as a profession, of all things, an auto mechanic! She would later say that helping me fiddle-faddle with my old Camaro in the garage as a child was what put the bug in her cap. And that being the case or not, her determination and ambition nonetheless saw the remarkable achievement of a Class A license and a position at the local Mercedes dealership before her twenty-second birthday.

Proud parents to be sure, her mother and I were nevertheless fully aware and had to admit that Karly's other most notable and distinguishing attribute was that she had a mouth on her that too often knew no boundaries. Unfortunately, it wasn't just the impressive list of expletives that would regularly come flying out of her but her unbridled willingness to fire them off in succession at anyone who'd had the audacity or misfortune of getting caught in her crosshairs on a bad day.

So, it came as no surprise to learn that some weeks earlier, while in a snit over a set of ignition keys incorrectly returned to the locker, Karly had dialed up the front desk to provide the "ill- witted" receptionist with a lambasting of biblical proportions. Unfortunately, so engrossed was she in her tyrannical tirade, that she'd failed to realize that somehow and unintentionally she had hit the intercom button for the entire showroom. The general manager, needing to initiate immediate damage control, was allegedly seen sprinting through the building, frantically weaving and winding his way in between prestigious cars and perplexed customers, with mask and muzzle in tow.

And while Diane, more or less tolerated that kind of language, the standing order around father, for all my children, was "*Zip It!*" Although Karly did try in earnest to maintain a lid on her cursing and cussing while in my presence, I would quite often find myself rolling my eyes up towards the heavens and shaking my head in amazement at what still slipped out through the cracks.

That morning I'd been watching the weather reports since well before sunrise, hoping for the best but expecting the worst as the gloomy skies of early December offer so few good days for flying. Believing that this time around we would be bringing home a kitten, I was pleased to see that the 6:00 am TAF— Terminal Area Forecast— for Kitchener/Waterloo was predicting marginal ceilings for most of the day. Whereupon, wasting no time, by the break of dawn and with cat carrier securely stowed away, we were once again airborne.

Unlike most smaller airports, including our own, Kitchener is a Control Zone, accommodating domestic and international flights. On that particular morning the air traffic controller had placed us in a holding pattern while giving clearance to larger aircraft, and so by the time we had finally landed Karly was already waiting at the FBO with Starbucks in hand!

An abundance of femininity notwithstanding, little in life could diminish Karly's inherent love for big machines and all things with motors. On account of this, and being the supportive parents that we always professed to be, we found ourselves, yet again, suffering the humiliation of having to climb up into and parade around in what I always referred to as *that ridiculous monster truck of hers*. Nonetheless, we were soon on our way and it wasn't long before we had arrived, turning into a mature neighbourhood of elegant Victorian homes that directly and decisively provided Diane and me with a welcome sense of assurance that this time around things were going to be different.

Counting up house numbers, we crept along the street, each of us making a visual estimation of which manor further down the way would be ours. Coming slowly into focus, one in particular began to attract our collective attention. Disparagingly distinguishing itself from the community of homes, it was for all intents and purposes *That House!* The one in so many films that neighbourhood children fearfully avoid and spin yarns about who lives inside and what nefarious nocturnal crimes they are committing. And having a bad feeling about where this was going, in unison, we nervously began calling out the remaining house numbers, "658...660...662...664...of course...666! Really?!"

From the curbside we took a minute to marvel at the considerable state of its disrepair. Aged and uncared for wooden siding had over time faded and cracked into a mournful grey. Worn and weary shutters crammed with leafless and lifeless vines hung haggardly aside overclouded windows. Uncounted seasons of sorrowful vegetation clasped haplessly from remnants of broken eavestroughs. And the grounds were an unkempt acreage of dying or dead trees overgrown with tattered shrubs and uncut grass that crept over a broken stone walkway. Indeed, an overall portrait of spooky that lacked only a small black storm cloud throwing down bolts of lightning upon it to complete the places' *Alfred Hitchcock motif.*

In for a penny in for a pound, I popped opened my door, slid off the seat and onto the running board, took a deep breath, and then jumped down several stories to the roadway. Safely there, I turned to render assistance to my dear wife by clasping her about the waist while she braced herself upon my shoulders and, working together, lifting and easing her carefully down onto the curb. A task that admittedly, at one point in our relationship, was accomplished with somewhat less difficulty.

Nearly obscured by a summer's long swath of overgrown grass, we, in single file, hopped and hurdled our way along the crumbled walk and up towards "*the old inn door.*"

Wherefrom the back of the line, Karly shouted out, "*Seriously, what kind of people own a mansion but can't afford a fucking lawnmower?*"

"Karly!" I barked back over my shoulder.

She returned from beneath a slight snigger an all too familiar, "Sorry Dad."

Accoutered with but only an old fashioned and tarnished brass door knocker, I cautiously gave it a careful tap but received no response. Twice more we rapped at the door but still no answer. Believing that a fourth knock would surely cause a little colony of bats to come flying out from the keyhole, we surmised that, for whatever the reason, no one was home and so we began to walk away — when suddenly, the door creaked and crept open.

A slightly weathered young woman with long black hair tied back into a bun appeared before us and began introducing herself, somewhat apologetically for the delay, as Sarah, the breeder.

Seemingly out of place and time, she and her home perfectly complemented each other in every eerily way. She wore a black skirt that hung like curled drapery just above a set of black ankle-laced boots and just below a sleeveless white Victorian blouse, pinned with a cameo at her neckline —effectively exposing a concerning collection of scratches and lacerations from the tips of her fingers to the tops of her arms. Which I presumed were caused either by her homicidal cats or her recently having been voodoo-vaulted into the adjacent hedgerow of thorn bushes.

Be that as it may, we were nevertheless asked to step inside, and to "please have a seat in the living area" — where oddly enough what sparsity of furniture there was, was covered in white linens. Honestly, the place felt like a mausoleum. The house was cold, dank, damp, and the century-old wood floors cracked and cackled as we tiptoed slowly over them. Giving one the feeling that, at any minute, a trap door would soon give way sending the three of us screaming and sliding into the cellar, where we would be horrified and mortified to see other kitten shoppers tied to a rack or pinned into iron maidens.

"I only have the one cub left and his mother is rather protective of him, not to mention in an unfriendly mood today as she doesn't like strangers—but I will try to bring him out." —she explained void of expression to the three of us sitting frightfully abreast, shoulder to shoulder on the sofa.

With the absence of significant furnishings, coupled with large rooms and towering ceilings, the astounding acoustics of the house now allowed us to clearly hear what was unfolding in the next room.

"Vana stop,"—hissing, growling—"I said stop!"—louder hissing, more growling, and then floor thumping. "No, Vana,"—significant hissing, growling, and more floor thumping!

It was at this point that Karly, with her hands tucked into the pockets of her hoodie, leaned onto my shoulder and whispered, "Dad, this woman and her cats are clearly nuts, and I don't think you want some demented kitten scratching your eyes out in the middle of the night, do you?"

Scorning back at her with that fatherly face that says, "you shouldn't talk of strangers that way," I was secretly thinking inside that she was making some seriously good points.

Having finally apprehended and negotiated the little demon away from its maleficent mother, Sarah returned, not cradling but clutching with both hands about his waist, a clearly distressed, frigid and rigid kitten that she introduced as "we call him Chucky."

"OMG, that figures!" Karly blurted out while inconspicuously elbowing me in the ribs.

"Would either of you like to try and hold him?"—she spotlight questioned the three stooges just sitting there, glancing back and forth at each other, hoping one or the other might stupidly volunteer.

"Of course, I will," my Diane, always the sucker...I

mean trooper, reluctantly but bravely offered. And not to anyone's surprise, just as she extended her hands to receive him, little Chucky dug his claws so deep into the skin of her palms that she began to immediately and profusely pour blood and bleed all over the linens.

Clearly and outwardly annoyed at my wife for having the effrontery to soil her sheets, Sarah promptly put down the kitten, who quickly tore away back to his mother while she then tore off to the kitchen to get some disinfectant and towels.

Fearing furtherance of insult or injury, and following the example of little Chucky, the three of us tore for the door— politely excused ourselves and headed out, tails tucked, back for home.

The following week Diane and I had returned once again empty-handedly disappointed from a third unsuccessful, albeit uneventful mission. After closing the hangar doors and climbing into the car, Diane suggested, "Hey, if you're hungry, we could take a drive up to Midland for a bite and check out a litter of kittens I saw for sale in the local classifieds today."

Inspired by her rare spontaneity and willingness to throw caution to the wind, not to mention the fact that I was famished, I willingly and eagerly agreed—and it wasn't long before we were sitting harbourside at one of our favourite digs, washing down a large pepperoni and green pepper with an ice-cold pint of Canadian Beer.

After a pleasant powwow, we quickly boxed up what was left, paid the bill, and by sunset had arrived at the breeder's quaint little house situated just on the outskirts of town. A polite and pleasant young woman welcomed us in and directed us to have a seat in the living room, while simultaneously shooing her two young children back to the dinner table.

Shortly after that she returned, clutching in her arms three still half-woken cubs, two males and a female, which she then properly plunked down on a large ottoman directly in front of us.

The two boys sprang to life almost instantaneously, and once having firmly gotten their bearings, leaped awkwardly to the floor and began chasing one another frantically about the room. In stark contrast, the female, who apparently wanted little or no part of her brothers' buffoonery, contrarily sat rather stylishly tall and quiet.

Conspicuously cloaked and clad with beautiful deep-black and silver exotic rosettes, she absolutely radiated a distinct air of regal sensibility. Clearly unimpressed by her siblings' juvenile clownery, especially while in the company of perfect strangers, she instead, rather auspiciously, cast up a pleading glance towards me that unmistakably begged, "*Please, get me the hell out of here!*"

Suddenly feeling confident that we'd stumbled upon an enchanted moment, I gently nudged Diane with my elbow and quietly whispered, "That's the one, the female."

"What? Are you sure Martin? Just like that?"

"Ya," smirking back at her, "just like that!"

Now speaking on behalf of my speechless spouse, I announced, "We'll take the female."

"Ok, great, you'll like her. She is a little slow to start

but once she gets going, you'll see that she has a really interesting personality."

There were those two words again, *interesting personality.* Of course, what we couldn't have known at that very moment in our lives was that "interesting personality" was just Bengal breeder code for—*We are now in deep, deep yogurt!*

All the same, as Diane headed off to the next room with the breeder to take care of the business of remuneration, vaccination and the education of feeding and other essentials, kitten and I curled up together to consider what might be a good name for her.

"What do you think kitten, what should we call you?" I asked while toggling up and down the screen of saved names I had since long ago compiled in anticipation of this very moment.

Clearly captivated by the moving lines, little kitten suddenly dashed out her paw onto the glass, definitively halting the scroll.

"Oh," I laughed, amused by her sudden sense of timing. "Is this the one that you want?" I snickered some more, then gently lifted and removed her paw so I could see what name she had, by chance, fortuitously chosen.

"Hmmm...Zahra! That's pretty, let's see what it means."

I tapped the definition tab —"*Zahra, from Arabic, meaning brilliant and bright.*"

Well, she nailed it, and from that moment on it was now showtime!

Kindred Spirit

I f we had held any ill-conceived concerns that Zahra might require a minute of adjustment or some time to settle in, they'd quickly have been forgotten, as the moment her paws hit the pavement she was away to the races!

Zahra, or Kitten as Diane preferred to refer to her when all was well with the world, began to immediately charm and endear herself to us in many ways. Certainly not the least of which was with her remarkable appearance, correctly hitched to a manner of movement and self-presentation that was unlike any we had ever seen before. Even as a kitten, Kitten had a kind of swagger, like a lion subtly sauntering across the hot plains of the Serengeti—as she mulled and meandered about exploring all the nooks and crannies of the house.

Moreover, we were fascinated and entirely captivated with her obvious intelligence, interwoven as it was with a near overabundance of self-confidence. Without hesitation, she swiftly and effortlessly mastered the little revolving cat door that led from the house to the garage where we kept her litter. Soon after that, she promptly self-declared and installed herself as the sovereign of our little kingdom as if she'd never belonged anywhere but precisely there.

But above all, it was her preposterous personality, arrived as it had on this earth with a factory-installed insatiable curiosity that demanded she investigate and be a part of absolutely everything and anything that we did.

And in those first few days, much to Diane's utter frustration, it was Zahra's relentless preoccupation with thrashing the daylights out of the Christmas tree that consumed so much of her precious energy.

A mirthful masterpiece well worthy of annual acclaim, it demanded of my dear Diane not less than an entire day of toiling and tinkering with tinsel and twine, hand-painted bulbs of all colours and designs —frost-covered balls and birch bark branches, feathers, pinecones, and red poinsettias. Pausing only long enough for a sip of her tea or baking up a batch of Christmas sugar cookies and hot chocolate dashed with wisps of whipped cream.

But for Zahra, all this fuss, muss, clutter and clatter was of little matter, except to present to her, in the end, only the grandest cat toy ever conceived or imagined.

Never veering far from the game plan, she would routinely begin by batting about the boxes and bags at the bottom of the tree, before bouncing up to the first base of branches and then *grinching* her way around and around, pattering and pawing at my poor companion's perfectly placed creations. Sometimes so vigorously would she bound up through the boughs, as to so shake the stand

and foundation, that it would cause several of Diane's precious ornaments to come tumbling and crashing to the floor. Carelessly callous of her Christmas criminality, she would just continue along, merrily making her way up to the tip of the summit, only to heartlessly dislodge the lit angel whilst replacing it with her very own head.

My poor spouse, routinely in a predictable panic, would take to running to her tree, cautiously and carefully extracting Kitten from somewhere deep inside— bits of tinsel and ribbon still clasped tightly in her little clutches.

Placing Zahra down onto the floor and holding her steady with one hand, while finger-pointing with the other, Diane would begin commanding, "No, Zahra, not the tree!" And once feeling positively sure that her message had been well received, conceived and understood, she would release Kitten. Whereby Kitten would then immediately spring back to the tree like a rubber band and begin the yuletide mugging all over again. From behind the scene, I'd try desperately to contain my laughter, so strenuously in fact, that I'm sure it wasn't good for me.

Mind you, not that I was spared either the frustrations of Kitten's particular brand of shenanigans. Precisely, because if Diane's tree was for Zahra a fascination and a preoccupation, my printer, on the other hand, was for her an absolute obsession.

Mounted on the floor of the cabinetry beside my chair, the moment I sent something to print, seemingly out of nowhere, she'd come flying across the room like a maniacal missile head first and directly into the paper tray— with only her grappling back paws and silly short tail sticking straight up and out. Not stopping there, she would then proceed, as if possessed, to crazily crumple and shred my documents, requiring I hastily extract her with what was left of my work still clasped in her claws. Having to regularly spend considerable time trying to unjam and clean up the carnage left behind, I eventually committed to placing several Post-It notes on my screen and the keyboard with the warning, *"Check for Kitten Before Printing!"*

Item number three on Zahra's to-do list was the dishwasher. Lest one of us open the door and retract the bottom rack, we'd soon turn back to see Kitten entangled amongst the plastic tines as if miraculously transported down from space. Resolutely refusing to vacate the operation, she insisted instead on inspecting every incoming glass or plate, pawing at the crockery as if to ensure their proper placement before the commencement of cleaning could begin.

And while the loading and unloading of the dishwasher with Kitten was often humorous and entertaining, we quickly realized the danger when it came to the washing machine and dryer. Because of course, the very minute either of the doors to each were opened, Zahra would dependably leap inside to initiate an excellent game of hide-and-seek amongst the clothing. So terrified were we that one of us would surely, and inevitably, at some point accidentally wash and dry our cat, that Diane soon installed another gathering of Post-It notes on the doors and all controls with the warning, *"Check for Kitten Before Starting"*!

By the end of each day in *full go mode*, Diane and I were genuinely astonished that, even at bedtime, Zahra had yet one more gear to shift into. Her favourite game began by secretly hiding behind and beneath our bedroom dresser, then covertly climbing up and into one of the drawers. And while to this day I still have no idea how she managed this incredible feat; she would nevertheless startle and surprise one of us to the point of a gasp while we went to retrieve our nightwear. Just as suddenly as she appeared, she would then vanish like *Houdini* seemingly into thin air, but only to then reappear minutes later in another drawer. So dependable was this bedtime tomfoolery that we soon felt it needed a name, and so we affectionately began referring to it as *Kitten Whack-a-Mole*.

Once we'd settled into bed, thank goodness, Zahra thankfully slept through the entire night—as even she by the laws of nature surely needed adequate time to fully recharge her batteries. However, her insistence on regular togetherness required that we tolerate her being wedged firmly in between us, back to back to back, until morning.

As one would expect, this considerable expenditure of energy called for regular bouts of refueling, so it made perfect sense that Kitten had an appetite no less in the extreme than everything else about her. To our amazement, she would regularly clean her plate to the point where we often wondered if we had forgotten to feed her in the first place. And as finicky as most cats are about food, Zahra was oppositely not! In fact, she soon began investigating and requesting samples of whatever Diane and I were having for breakfast, lunch, or dinner. Despite a firm understanding of the evils that feeding from the table can bring, we nevertheless found it difficult to resist her pathetic pleas and soon found ourselves offering her little tasters of this or that.

Well it wasn't long before we had developed a pretty good idea of what Zahra's favourite foods were, and given her royal bloodlines, we were hardly surprised that shrimp cocktail, boeuf bourguignon and butter croissants topped the list. That being said, nothing got Kitten's culinary motor revving more than seeing the dessert tray come rolling into the dining room. I'll tell you this cat had a sweet tooth the likes of which we couldn't have possibly imagined— but admittedly and rest assured so did Diane and I, and I have to admit that some of my fondest memories with Kitten in those first few weeks together was sharing a bowl of rice pudding with cinnamon sprinkles while watching the evening news.

In fact, so much so did the three of us enjoy bonding around our confectionary compulsions that we soon began bringing Zahra along whenever Diane's craving for ice cream had us tripping into town for a Dairy Queen drive thru. And as smart as Kitten was, she soon figured out that putting coats on after dinner, more often than not, meant a Kitten cone was coming her way and thus was regularly and dependably found waiting impatiently ahead of us at the doorway.

But of all the good things that Zahra possessed, the one trait she often lacked was patience, and it never was more apparent than when having to wait for her order at the window. Routinely, she would take to standing on my lap, her front paws on the door, careening her neck nearly right into the establishment and clearly wondering, *"What the hell could be taking so long?"*

On one memorable trip while the DQ staff were once again testing Kitten's patience, she, for whatever her reasons, had decided that enough was enough and without so much as a meow of warning leaped from my lap and bound from the car through the window and directly into the restaurant!

"Oh my God!" Diane shouted out, as a commotion of employees began scampering and scattering about the kitchen desperately trying to recapture our cat. Diane and I, just sitting in the car, and dumbfounded as to what to do or how to help, felt a great sense of relief when thankfully the store manager had quickly gotten a hold of her.

Clearly not impressed with us, he, with a silently scornful scowl upon his face, then passed Kitten, and her cone, back out to us through the pickup window. On the ride home, while enjoying our treats, we amused ourselves at the thought of the bewildered people in the car behind us, who must have been shocked to see that Dairy Queen had added Bengals to the menu.

As Zahra was slowly turning our empty nest upside down and persistently proving that everything we believed about owning a cat at this stage of our lives was false, we had to admit that we were becoming quite enamored and fond of this little soul with all the entertainment and endearment she had to offer us.

The one concern that soon cropped up and created between Diane and me an impasse of opinions, was how to deal with Zahra wanting to go outside. It went without saying that her desire to be with us at all times became an issue should we decide to go out without her, often causing her to regularly try and slip out through the opened doorway whenever she got the chance.

And although Diane more or less agreed with the breeder that because of the dangers of predatory birds and coyotes, or even someone potentially taking her for her value, she ought to remain inside, effectively becoming a housebound cat. I on the other hand had a hard time with that. I found it challenging to think of poor Kitten having to watch from behind glass as a myriad of playthings teased and taunted her on some glorious spring morning.

Debating over what to do, I frequently tried to reason that Zahra, at some point, was going to get out through an open door or window and that acclimatizing her to the outdoor surroundings might possibly help her from getting lost should she do so.

One evening around that time, Diane arrived at home from shopping and after having put the bags onto the kitchen counter pulled out a small harness attached to a retractable lead line and plastic handle.

"Oh you've got to be kidding me?" I responded with an expression of *"this is a ridiculous idea"* about my face.

"Don't look at me like that. You want her to go outside, then you train her to use this!"—then tossed it at me with that all too familiar, "I'm not kidding Martin," bravado of hers.

Well, the following morning Zahra had woken me up near the break of dawn by sitting on my chest and swatting at my cheeks, suggesting we ought to get some breakfast. Somewhat begrudgingly, I slid out of bed, slipped on my bathrobe, and made my way into the kitchen to restock her kibble and mix up a dish of sultry salmon. Now that I was up anyway, I decided to make myself a tea, and shortly after that, the two of us took a moment to admire the blustering flakes of snow dancing about and blowing past the windows by the front door.

With Kitten captivated by the movements outside, it occurred to me that perhaps this might be an opportune time to test out Diane's ridiculous contraption.

At first, I just dangled the silly thing in front of her, making her chase it around, believing that if she got comfortable enough she might not go completely crazy when next I try and strap her into it. Surprisingly enough, this went relatively well, and so with little or no objection I was soon tossing cat toys about the front foyer, firmly towing and tugging behind her as she chased after them.

Now believing myself to be a natural cat trainer, I decided to test Kitten and the witless widget out on the front step—and so, donning *absolutely nothing* except my bathrobe and a pair of winter boots, we stepped outside.

As one might expect, Zahra thought this was great fun —and not wanting to stifle her eager exuberance, I let her lead me along the walkway down the driveway and then out onto the road, stopping just at the front of the house next door. Then suddenly, out of the corner of my eye, I caught wind and took notice of our dear neighbours, now gathering along with their three young children at their front window, gawking and gaping at me and surely wondering, "What the hell is Martin doing outside in his bathrobe walking his cat down the street in a blizzard?"

Realizing how ridiculous this must look and suddenly feeling seriously embarrassed, I began to quickly reel Kitten in. But, and as one would expect, Zahra wanted no part of that as it was going in the wrong direction— and like a landed fish on a dock, she frantically began flipping and flopping around.

"Zahra, stop it!" I commanded her, but this only angered her and made her more resistant. Desperate to just get the hell out of there, I resorted to dragging her, with claws dug in, struggling and straining, little heaps of snow piling up over the fronts of her front paws and finally to the foot of my feet. Then unexpectedly, just as I bent over to pick her up, a giant gust of whirling wind came cruising along that blustered and blew my robe up and over my head—exposing in its entirety my bare naked ass, plainly and pathetically to my surely ashamed neighbours, cringeworthy-covering the eyes of their children.

Humbled and humiliated, I now found myself frantically struggling to contain Zahra in one hand while frantically trying to keep the coattails of my robe down with the other. But as I turned and headed for home, the bloody wind blew up again, blowing open the front of my robe so wide that it demanded and required I immediately place Kitten in front of my *naughty bits* to avoid having someone call the authorities.

Amidst the fracas, I hadn't noticed two cars loaded with holiday families that had stopped to watch the show. Embarrassed beyond belief, all I could do was point the blame at Kitten tuck my tail and head for the house.

Once inside I proceeded directly to the bedroom, unloaded Zahra down onto the bed beside Diane and angrily recounted what had just happened to me as a result of her dumb idea.

Irritated and confused as I was that she had no response, it took of course a moment of silence for me to realize that she was actually laughing so hard into her pillow that she was physically unable to do so.

Nonetheless, having had to suffer through this horrendously horrible ordeal, I eventually used it to my advantage by negotiating and accommodating an agreement on the matter of Kitten and the great outdoors.

"Ok, Hun, you can take Zahra outside without a leash, so long as, and I mean it Martin, you are right there with her!"

Of Felines and Fellows

The following morning Zahra and I were once again up together in the early bright—this time around sitting around the kitchen table and deliciously devouring the last savory square of leftover lasagna— when unexpectedly, a little field mouse scurrying about the pottery on the back deck caught our attention.

Now, if felines and fellows have one thing in common, it is undoubtedly an innate, albeit primeval, instinct for the hunt. Frequently misunderstood and even occasionally reviled by the fairer sex, it nonetheless empowers a bond between man and beast that's well, just a lot of fun!

Predictably then, and only seconds later, the two of us could be seen with foreboding faces pressed against the glass of the back door, closely and carefully surveying the situation, detailing and drawing up a plan of engagement.

Despite fully understanding and appreciating the fact that I'd surely be read the Riot Act if I let Kitten out to have a little chase, I foolishly reasoned to myself that supervision, regardless of which side of the window I was on, was supervision nonetheless—right?

Apparently not so, because I'll tell you, no sooner did I let Zahra slip out that back door than there came careening across the living room a velocity of volume that nearly caused me to buckle and crumble in full incapacitation.

"Martin! Did you let that cat out!?"

Caught red-handed and in clear violation of the prime directive, all I could offer back was, "What? I'm watching right here from the window."

Boy if looks could kill! Scorning, scowling and growling, she marched across the living room, picking up along the way Zahra's little fish and fishing rod cat toy that Kitten was so fond of, slipped and stomped on a pair of winter boots and then went storming out past me to retrieve her.

Well, I thought to myself, not much point in the two of us out there freezing to death and so resumed back to the business of mopping up the last of the lasagna—keeping of course one eye closely on the rather comical scene of Diane trying to persuade and procure Zahra away from her pursuit of the little mouse and back into the safety and security of the house.

"Fat chance of that happening," I chuckled and said to myself— when all of a sudden and like a shot little *Ratatouille* tore down the steps of the decking with Zahra, as one would expect, bounding behind in hot pursuit.

Not once but twice around the stone firepit they went, then underneath the shed, out on the other side and finally across the yard and into the bushes behind the large propane cylinder at the side of our property.

"Now look what you've done," she bored at me with daggers in her eyes. Then, turning herself around and latching onto the railing with both hands, she carefully began sidestepping her way down the snow-covered steps to have after her.

"Oh crap", I said to myself— and not wanting to spend a back- breaking night on the sofa, I immediately made for the closet, quickly threw on my parka and boots and with all possible dispatch exited the back doorway to help with the rescue and recovery. However, in such a hurried hurry was I that halfway down the damn frozen staircase, I lost my footing and went flying, feet first, bumping, thumping, slipping and dumping down to the very bottom on my backside.

Lying in a heap of agony, it took me a minute of strain and struggle to get back onto my feet. As I stood there cursing cold and country, I soon caught ear of Diane's cries, now full-belly-straddled over and across the top of the tank, feet flailing in the air while still trying to tease and taunt Zahra back out from the thorny bushes on the other side. For whatever the exact scientific reason, I really couldn't be sure, perhaps the heat from her body began liquifying and slickifying the ice on the tank, but the simple fact of the matter was that she was now beginning to slide over the tank and into the thorny bushes patched on the other side!

"Shit!" As fast as I could, I hopped and lopped over the frozen tundra that was our yard and just in the nick of time managed to get a hold of her by the ankles of her boots. With all my might I began to haul and heave, but to little avail, as the snowy surface left me struggling for traction. This now demanded that I leave one foot firmly planted while bracing the other up against the tank to lever some leverage. Of course, just as I assumed the position, I again took notice of my neighbours who had quickly gathered along with their children at their sliding glass door, gawking, gaping, and surely wondering, *What the hell is Martin up to now?!*

The simple laws of physics could easily have predicted what was coming next, begging only the question, *how soon and how bad?*

Simply put, one person tugging on a pair of untied galoshes, loosely attached to another person lingering over a fuel tank and caught in a well of gravity, will inevitably, at some point soon, see the two bodies fly apart in opposite directions. As surely as one would expect, I swiftly and suddenly went sailing in one direction with a pair of empty boots in my hands, while my poor Diane went somersaulting over the tank and piling into the bushes with the little fishing cat rod still clenched in hers.

Quickly clambering and climbing up and over the tank, I peered down upon the poor barefooted and lifeless body of my wife lying amid the shrubbery and asked, "Oh my God Hun, are you alright?" When suddenly out from the shadows Zahra appeared and perhaps feeling partly to blame for the whole affair, took to Diane's side offering what comfort she could. As I offered to do the same, I was instead promptly and angrily handed the cat and then ordered to take her back inside before something else happened!

WITH CHRISTMAS now only a week away, Diane soon forgave, forgot and began refocusing her attention to the staggered arrival of our children and their significant others for a short stay at our house over the holidays.

Strangely, it was around this time that Zahra, despite her predatory prowess, began to exhibit an immature and almost infantile need to suckle in the middle of the night. What started as a mild annoyance of damp blankets and icky pillowcases soon became more unsettling as Kitten quickly migrated from linens to *human earlobes* as her pacifier of choice.

Of this it could be said that Zahra and I quickly came to an understanding that in no way, shape or form were my ears going to become a makeshift binky for anyone—which of course left Diane's lobes as the only supply of binkies in the house.

Regularly having to go it alone when defending herself against Kitten's nocturnal vampire-like tendencies, Diane soon became frustrated as no matter what she tried, the problem steadfastly refused to go away.

Besides the simple botheration of the matter, the bigger problem for my wife was that Kitten's dander, while at a distance or even on her lap was tolerable, up close and personal around her face dependably caused an allergic reaction that resulted in swollen eyes and a stuffy nose.

Having exhausted all practical means to resolve this

odd quandary, Diane eventually took to the drastic measure of having to attire herself in an eclectic assortment of protective headwear before going to bed. This included the bright yellow earmuffs I used to do yard work in the summer, a pair of geriatric sunglasses fitted with peripheral panels, and a colourful Christmas scarf tied about her neck and beautiful face.

Forced to sleep on her back throughout the night so as not to accidentally displace any of her equipment, this quite naturally caused her to snore more indignantly. And for me, unaccustomed to the disturbing imagery, it frequently left me spooked should I require a midnight trip to the loo.

Well, on the last business day before the weekend leading up to Christmas, Diane had gone to bed that night before nervously awaiting the arrival of essential documents by courier the following morning. Earlier than expected, our loud clanging doorbell began chiming that startled us from our sleep.

Diane, not wanting to miss the delivery, sat straight up in bed and in a half-woken panic began exclaiming, "Oh my God, that's the courier!" Lying on my side, I looked back over my shoulder towards her, and squinting in the morning light muttered,

"Take off your muffs."

"What?" she said.

"Take off your muffs," I repeated.

"What?" she said.

Exhausted, I just waved my hand at her and went back to snoozing.

Still dazed and confused, she then leaped from the bed and raced to the doorway, where she unexpectedly found not the courier but instead an assemblage of Jehovah's Witnesses—themselves wondering, no doubt, why this woman had arrived to greet them attired in Winnie the Pooh pajamas and a headful of *welding gear.*

Wanting of course to make the most of an open-door opportunity, Zahra naturally shot right out through from between Diane's feet and down the walkway. In fear of not following her own decrees and directives on free-ranged Kitten, she quickly kicked on a pair of pink slippers and went tearing out after her—bowling through the congregation of faithful followers, still decked in her headwear, fumbling and bumbling behind Zahra, crying out, "No Kitten No!"

But Zahra, having little intentions of being recaptured too soon, instead barreled down the driveway and with Diane still wailing and trailing behind, leaped onto and then up the trunk of the big Maple at the end of our lane — scampering and finally perching herself on a branch high up above.

By now all the commotion had captured my curiosity, and it wasn't long before I found myself enrobed at the open front door face to the backs of an audience of Jehovah's piously pondering the divine denotation of what they were, well, *Witnessing!*

"Martin!" Diane desperately insisted on me from across the front lawn. "If she goes any higher we will have to phone the fire department!"

God, not wanting that to happen, I "*good morning-ed*"

and pardoned my way past the flocking Jehovah's and quickly to the garage to retrieve the extendable ladder.

"Hurry!" I could hear Diane yelling as I frustratingly struggled to unhook the damn thing from the hinges on the wall—eventually doing so and arriving at the cat crisis, placing and protracting it out precariously up against the tree.

"I'll hold the base while you go up and get her."

"Really Hun? No kidding!" I answered back with a spat of sarcasm before escalating my way up the rungs on the stairway to heaven! "Come here Kitten," I calmly and caringly asked of a surprisingly cooperative Zahra, who without hesitation meowed and maneuvered herself back into my arms.

Impossible as it sounds, at that very moment as we began our descent down, our neighbours and their children drove out their drive and with all their faces pressed up against the car window were gaping, gawking and rubbernecking as they slowly went by.

No harm, no foul and later that afternoon, with a stack of religious reading material in hand and just about the time the courier had come and gone, our son Talon arrived along with his long time fiancé, Joanna.

"Hey Dad, what's up with the ladder?" he inquisitively inquired before dropping his gear at the floor of the door and pushing past me directly and determinedly straight for the refrigerator.

His Joanna, on the other hand, always took the time to meet and greet us with an abundance of much appreciated hugs and hellos. As an only child of Polish immigrants, she was mannerly raised with all the traditions and values of her community, and as such, she invariably arrived at our house not only politely and impeccably dressed but, more importantly, packed and saddled with a basket full of homemade goodies. Diane and I, like the Pavlovian dog, would soon begin salivating as we watched her unpack and dish out some of our favourites— including of course potato and onion perogies topped with heaps of sour cream.

Our son bless his soul, unlike his two younger sisters, had long since made up his mind that a formal education and a career were in no way a match for a life as a successful self-made entrepreneur! Being that the apple doesn't fall far from the tree, his mother and I were hardly surprised as he'd routinely venture off into the unknown in the pursuit of his happiness.

Unfortunately, like his very own father at that age, he frequently refused to heed his elders' advice and as such was very often doomed, of course, to learn it the hard way. For Talon and Joanna, this regrettably produced a curriculum vitae full of false starts that included: *self - betterment and business seminars, fix and flip it how to real estate investment programs and soda pop pyramid schemes* to mention only a few. After years of considerable cost and frustration, they finally seemed to be in the running with the manufacturing and online marketing of portable beach windscreens— a launchpad for a host of other related products under the growing brand of **Beach Fence**!

Given all the stress and strain of starting their own business, a four-day Christmas micro-vacation at our house was likely just what the doctor had ordered, and as such, the two of them naturally exhausted had retired early to bed that evening.

Having forgotten to warn them, nor remembering to shut their bedroom door that night, they arrived at the breakfast table the following morning clearly distressed and utterly unimpressed at now having to wear for the holidays, a matching set of red and swollen Christmas *ear bulbs!*

Tannen Bombed

J ust as the plates of over-easies, maple bacon and Texas toast were making their way from the skillet to the breakfast table, our middle daughter and her younger sister Karly had promptly arrived with forks, knives, and hunger in hand.

Heidi, a beautiful image of the name we'd given her, with bright blue eyes and waist-length blonde hair, had recently finished her education and was working in Toronto as a psychotherapist, lecturing and helping people with obsessive compulsive disorders.

For me, this was always a conundrum of sorts, as I had little doubts that she suffered from the very same affliction when it came to that little dog of hers, Max. It was always *Moo Moo* this or *BoBo* that, he was continually at her feet and she talked about him incessantly. So much so that she would slip slides of Max into her lectures, having then to *accidentally* speak about him with her class.

A curly cockapoo, I always argued that Max himself should have been on Heidi's client list for compulsive disorders, as for him, it was never, and I mean never, not about the food. From the second he arrived until the minute he left, Max would sit at the border of the kitchen gaping, afraid even to blink as he might miss a morsel coming his way. Since I often did much of the cooking, this would dependably drive me around the bend. Even turned away, I could feel his beady little eyes boring into the back of my head and so routinely I could be heard hollering for Heidi.

She would hastily arrive, scoop him up, kiss and pat him, then, while in baby talk, console him, "Oh *BoBo*, are you driving daddy crazy" as if he were the injured party. She would then put him down where only minutes later, scheming and seizing on the opportunity, he would skulk away from her attention and quietly return to his station staring into the kitchen.

And as much as Max wanted to be with food, he in the antithesis, wanted absolutely zilch to do with cats. Raised as an orphan together with a litter of pestering kittens that considered him their personal punching bag, he desperately tried to ignore Zahra at all costs. Kitten, who contrarily demanded nothing less than Max's full and undivided attention, quickly became angered and annoyed at his stubborn refusal to acknowledge her and would thus begin to tease and taunt him relentlessly.

Her harassments began by hiding stealthily beneath the sofa and eagle eyeballing poor *MooMoo* famished-parked at the gates of heaven only some few feet away. Once confidently sure his attention had become entirely and affectionately affixed to the cookery, she would explode from the starting gate and tear across the living room, launching herself into the air with arms fully extended and tackle poor Max to the ground. Vehemently vexed, he would take to whining, growling and barking at her before chasing Kitten back under the couch—then without hesitation, dutifully returning to his post guarding the galley.

And so, with the animals in anarchy, the jazzy Christmas carols caroling, our children boisterously blabbering around the kitchen table, laughing and telling stories that rarely included their parents— who they themselves, were busy anyway butlering back and forth snacks, drinks and dirty dishes—giving it their all just to maintain some assemblage of order in a home where bags of washing, gizmos and gadgets, boxes and baskets, footwear and headwear, makeup, hair clips, headphones and headsets spontaneously burst into existence. Once again faithfully and tragically transforming our otherwise peacefully perfect empty nest into the Christmas *helliday-household* I knew it would become. That is of course until someone inevitably stumbled onto the critical question of who was on the guestlist for Christmas dinner—and more specifically, whether or not my mother was coming?!

For anyone who ever knew her hardly could they argue that without a doubt my mother was at very least *a one of a kind*, albeit in an ambiguous sort of way. On a rare good day she was an outgoing, positive and energetic spirit. But, more often than not, her determination for getting *royally sauced* and then sermonizing to anyone within earshot about precisely who was to blame for the ills of the world routinely and regrettably left most of us running for cover.

As she migrated into her senior years and what eventually became a near daily routine, began with the faithful administration of several ounces of Canadian rye into her morning coffee. By late afternoon, once two or more bottles of pinot noir had fallen by the wayside, anyone inside or close to the fallout zone would inescapably be subjected to her *All in the Family* style tyrannical orations!

Her poor husband Herb, of many years, and a quiet and gentle soul, was too frequently the sole beneficiary of her daily discourses. Eventually, he himself, unable to escape the regular barrage of *incoming*, found and took frequent refuge within the last remnants of mother's rye.

Unfortunately, for ourselves and the children, family get- togethers therefore too often became a powder-keg with all of us tiptoeing around trying desperately not to set off Oma's fuse after she'd had had one too many.

Making the matter worse was that that year Diane's parents, sister, nieces and nephews had decided to join my family side. And my father-in-law was the sort that loved to entertain himself by impolitely poking at people until he had gotten himself firmly under their skin. Factor in the attendance of my own father— a crusty, criticizing Austrian from an old country of values that had me as a child off to the woods more than once to find the switch that he would then let me have it with—and you now had a predictable pressure cooker that needed only a loosely lit fuse to blow her top.

Nevertheless, and hoping for the best, we pressed on and it wasn't long before Christmas morning was soon upon us.

As tradition would have it Talon became St. Nick and quickly began handing out presents from beneath the tree to everyone in their pyjamas, sipping on hot chocolate topped with whip cream and candy sprinkles. Zahra was absolutely beside herself with excitement, ripping and tearing through discarded wrapping paper and ribbons, leaping in and out of empty boxes and sorting through a kitten-load of kitten toys from everyone. Even Max, caught up in the madness, managed to forget about food, at least for a little while anyway.

Once all the hubbub and hoopla of opening presents had finally settled down, and after Diane and I had sufficiently gone about bagging the debris, we were ready for act two of the Christmas day operation. In other words, it was turkey time!

As much as Diane's annual Christmas tree was a vision of beauty for our eyes to behold, her annual Christmas day dinner was an absolute feast of culinary delights for us to savour. For three days her bird had already been bagged, bucketed and brined hush-hush in a secret marinade of ciders and spices. Long before noon, she'd start stuffing the stuffing out of the stuffing and begin preparing the mainstay of traditional side dishes, including mashed potatoes, dilled corn, carrots and greens, Yorkshire pudding for her family side and schnitzel and dumplings for mine. Thankfully, for Diane, dessert was not on her to-do list as most everyone brought a homemade recipe that dependably included cherry cheesecake, chocolate, and lemon pies—and my favorite, of course, apple strudel.

With Diane then fully embedded in making supper, stage three of the whole affair with all its duties and responsibilities rested entirely on my shoulders as the head of the social committee. As such, I was solely in charge of answering the door, collecting coats, mixing and refilling drinks, replenishing nut and chip bowls, conversing, entertaining and, most importantly, keeping a careful eye on mother's intake of alcohol.

As the house filled up with guests that afternoon, all the buzz of laughter and conversation was electrifying not only the house, but to our amazement, our Zahra as well. Instantaneously transforming into the socialite of the year, she insisted on meeting and greeting everyone who arrived at the door— vaingloriously strutting about while fluffing up and flaunting her new fur coat.

Then, for some unknown impetus that I couldn't quite fathom, perhaps when no one was looking she'd been helping herself to unguarded liquor and liquors, Kitten nonetheless viciously began attacking people's feet—and I mean viciously, full fang and claw merciless mangling! Chunking down on a toe with her sharp little teeth so forcefully, it would cause poor guests to wince and cry out in pain. Vaulting again from my chair, I would angrily shoo Zahra away with my arms, where stubbornly she would merely puff and stack up sideways with her hair and tail standing straight up, ears pinned back, dancing back and forth like a boxer in the ring challenging me to throw the first punch.

At first I'd try to laugh off her ridiculous posing and posturing before pleading with her to "please go away and leave people alone." Likely by now three sheets to the wind, she had of course no intentions of doing this and rather merely went directly back to targeting another sole. Oddly enough and for whatever the reason, perhaps the scent of booze oozing from her pores and into her socks like a sack full of catnip, it was mother's feet that soon bore the full brunt of Zahra's muggings.

After several repeated salvos, my mother was becoming outwardly agitated and angry, even at one point pulling Kitten off by the scruff of her neck. Making matters worse was that she had somewhere in between assaults found, opened and dispensed several shots of Jägermeister! Naturally, Diane's dad smelling blood in the water, was busy fueling her fire by twitting her views on politics and religion, while tag-teaming off and on with my father casting in with callous criticisms about her indulgent drinking.

Realizing all hell was about to break loose, I once again, scooped up Kitten, apologized profusely and then seeking some guidance, made my way to the kitchen to find Diane— now frantically stirring several percolating pots of potatoes and gravy.

"Di," I whispered quickly and quietly. "Do you know what our little culprit here is doing? She is maliciously and manically molesting my mother's feet!"

Where thereupon came swiftly and directly barreling back my loving wife's supportive response. *"Hun, I'm making gravy deal with it!"*

Having now to make an executive decision I took Zahra downstairs to a clustered cluster of self-indulgent millennials and demanded, "Listen guys, before Kitten Christmas-cripples your grandmother, can you please play with Zahra until dinner is ready—thank you!"

Thankfully it wasn't long after that that Diane had rung the dinner bell, effectively redirecting everyone's focus to the task of queuing up and around the plates and pans of goodies, before then taking their place at the dining table.

Poorly positioned directly across from my father and now swilling on a swelling glass of cabernet sauvignon, my mother was having a hard time letting go of what was said only minutes ago and so began, "If someone had just spent more time thinking about their children instead of himself."

"Mum!" I interrupted, slightly smiling and gently nodding, trying to inconspicuously convey, "Not now, please!"

Tannen-bombed as she plainly was, I had to credit her for her efforts to avoid making a scene by instead diffusing her anger and frustration by quietly, though rather nervously, twitching her feet beneath the table.

As one could have predicted, this was what Kitten, likely Tannen-bombed herself, was precisely waiting for. Without warning and with all the might she could muster, she pounced like a Bengalize tiger pounding down onto and into my mother's poor foot.

Needless to say, there was the dreaded fuse we had all been dreading!

Screaming and shrieking in a burst of sudden pain, she

went jetting and jolting back in her chair, hurtling and hurling up her arms, sending red vino splashing and splattering all over the ceiling, the dinner table and even our guests.

Expounding her pent-up rage, she leaped to her feet, grabbed hold of the wooden cooking spoon, and while cursing Kitten with every slur-word she could muster, promptly had after her.

Unbalanced by her haughty helpings of Christmas cheer, she managed only to bumble and stumble a few feet before stubbing her toe firmly into the leg of the coffee table. Now spinning around in the second wave of shrieking agony, she soon lost her balance, twisted, turned, and then went face-timbering and mother-meshing deep into the branches of Diane's beloved Christmas tree. The force of the impact so stringent, it easily dislodged the tree from the stand, sending it and mother, slamming and bouncing off the wall, careening and crashing with all the lights and decor, firmly down to and all over the floor!

A mad rush from everyone at the table quickly ensued to mother's side to offer what assistance and sympathy we could. Still wrangling beneath the tree and wondering what the hell just happened, we all slowly helped her out from under the tangle of tinsel and back onto her feet.

Relieved to see it was mostly just mother's pride that was injured, we all turned back and headed for the dinner table, only to see Kitten at my mother's chair and as karma would have it, helping herself to a helping of her turkey.

. . .

THAT FIRST CHRISTMAS with Zahra was undoubtedly one for the books and not soon to be forgotten, but somehow, we did manage to make it peacefully through the remainder of the holidays.

And as January's deep freeze slowly surrendered itself to the wearisome dark nights of February, we found little else to do but watch as Kitten nestled into our bed, while visions of Kitten Cones surely danced in her head—and Diane in her kerchief and I in my cap, once again settled in too for a long winters nap.

More Canine than Cat

As the long and fettering arms of old man winter finally began to loosen their grip, we welcomed with open hearts the warmer days of spring, the return of the apple blossoms, the chatter of the chickadees and the effervescent aromas of the white and violet lilacs dancing through the air.

Zahra too had managed a magnificent metamorphosis. Transforming from the devilishly adorable kitten we'd brought home only six months earlier, into a handsome young Bengal cat, resplendent in posture and now flourishing the un-canniest of intellects!

More canine than cat, one of Zahra's favourite digs was to accompany Diane and me on walks out through the hollow in the forest at the back of our property and along the rows of newly planted Kris Kringle pines down unto and around the old fishing pond.

Kindly offered to the residents of our rural community by the farmer as a place for people to stroll along or walk their dogs, we would on occasion, cross paths with someone leashing their mutt who were predictably astonished to see us walking our cat.

"Is that your cat? That's amazing, she just follows you?"

Routinely they'd go on interrogating us while concurrently trying to restrain their boorish slobbering and whimpering pooch clambering to get at Zahra, who in the alternative always sat peacefully untethered, undaunted and unimpressed at the heels of our feet.

Ambling on along we'd tootle and loop around the pond, dabbling in and out of the forest paths, before gradually making our way back to the house— pausing only now and then to wait for Zahra, should nature's call come calling.

Having unearthed, to her liking, a particularly well-sanded tree bed, Kitten would duck in and out of sight behind a sapling for a quick two-minute pit stop, fully expecting of course, that the expedition would take a knee while she did her business. Should Diane or I make the impertinent mistake however of forging on ahead without her, we'd soon receive a good rapping on the knuckles from Kitten, who now needed to interrupt her essential duty, leap back out onto the path and angrily yell at us to "*wait up!*"

So much so did the three of us enjoy palling around together, that we frequently even took Zahra along with us should an exceptionally calm morning provide the privilege of a fly-in breakfast. Ridiculously outfitted in her little catty-helmet with sewn-in cotton ball ear protectors that Diane had designed and knitted, we'd hungrily make the eight-minute hop up and over to the Collingwood airfield dinner. With Kitten on a leash for safety, we'd soon park ourselves at a picnic bench near the edge of the apron enjoying a panoramic view of the incoming planes, set and ready to dive into a stack of pancakes dripping with Zahra's favourite, whipped butter and maple syrup.

And as Kitten's almost human-like intelligence continued to grow, she sought out in each one of us that spent time with her, an intrinsic interest or personal characteristic to which she could both bond and better her understanding of humanity.

With me, it was my love of music and a passion for playing guitar that really struck a chord with Kitten, so to speak. Oddly enough, my favourite place and time to rehearse my parts for the band I played in was out in the quiet of the garage, long before the sun or even the birds had woken up. Without fail, Zahra would dependably come popping through the little cat door from the house into the garage, then leap up onto the top of my Marshal stack, pawing at the strings of my guitar while I tuned and tinkered with the tones of the amplifier.

Four hours, my faithful audience of one would sit and intently listen, as I played along with the music and the songs we were practicing. And on mornings that we were both feeling particularly salty, and a track or two had gotten our rock and roll mojos really going, we'd give it some serious volume that would not only shake the house but quite often wake the neighbours.

In Diane, Kitten found a perfect childhood companion

and playmate. Each of them having inherited and innate love of silly games, they would regularly spend time together playing or learning new tricks. To the former, pounce was undoubtedly a favourite.

"Martin, come here and watch this." Diane would giggle while fetching me away from whatever I was doing and make me spectate as she placed Zahra atop the headboard of our bed and then tinkled her fingers beneath the blankets. Instinctively Kitten would start wiggling back and forth her butt—intensely focusing and waiting for the precise moment to leap straight up into the air, narrowly evading contact with the ceiling fan before then pouncing down with all her might. Of course, never entirely satisfied with the quality of the first or second pounce, Diane would hesitantly shout at me as I began to edge away, "Wait, wait," then quickly reset kitten atop the headboard hoping to better the score.

Given her wit, teaching Kitten then to fetch came without much bother, and so it was with little surprise that Diane, having seen a commercial of a cat ringing a bell for food one day, soon decided and committed herself to training Zahra to do the very same.

Using a front-desk bellhop bell that she had allocated from — god knows where—Diane would repeatedly lift Kitten onto the coffee table in the living room and after placing the bell in front of her, she would take Zahra firmly by the paw and tightly tap it down onto the dinger — of course making it ring and then rewarding her with pats, kisses and a selection of tender morsels.

Undeterred by a lack of immediate success, Diane

relentlessly pressed on for several more days, until finally her frustrations had gotten the better of her.

"Martin, why isn't she getting this?—gavelling her fist onto the table. "I don't understand what I am doing wrong?"

I on the other hand invariably had little doubts that Zahra knew precisely what was being asked of her, but had decided that no-one, not even Diane, was going to denigrate her down into actually having to work for a living. In fact, not only did Kitten resist and refuse to ring my exasperated wife's bell but would take to batting the damn thing across the table and onto the floor when she'd finally had enough of the lessons.

Notwithstanding a no-holds-barred, succeed at all costs or die trying mentality, after a week or so of this nonsense, Diane eventually threw in the towel and admitted defeat.

That particular evening, once the armistice had been officially signed and sealed, we'd retreated to our bed for the night only to be awoken at the unholy hour of 2:00 am by a diabolical "ting!"

"Oh my God Martin, did you hear that?"

Springing from the bed like a madwoman, she went charging out into the living room overjoyed at the wondrous site of Zahra sitting by the bell and awaiting her reward. After providing Kitten with payment and after more than several minutes of jubilation and self-congratulations, Diane, tickled pink, eventually returned to bed.

When, of course, only moments later, "ting!"

"Ha-ha, she's so smart." Laughing and leaping from the bed like a schoolgirl then racing out to reward Kitten yet once more.

"Smart is right, who's training who!" I hollered out, desperately wanting to get some sleep!"

"Ok, ok, I'll put a dish of food out for her."

Skipping back minutes later and sliding beneath the covers, "That should settle her."

"Why don't you just put the bell in a drawer?" I suggested.

"You're kidding right, that might confuse her training."

"Her training?"

Thankfully all finally quieted down, and just as I began to drift back into blissful slumber. . ." ting."

"OMG—please ignore her Diane!"

Then "ting," and then "ting-ting," a momentary pause and then, "ting-ting, ting-ting-ting-ting-ting-ting-ting-ting-ting!"

Henceforth the bellhop bell spent its evenings blissfully slumbering in the drawer of my bedside night table!

Falling not far from the matriarchal tree, Talon was every bit as much the gamester as his mother. Inheriting, as her prodigy and for good measure, a compulsive need to succeed at whatever got into his head. And oddly enough, what began to emerge as a child and steadfastly manifested into his adulthood, was humorously, an almost obsessive determination to break his own record at anything that caught his attention.

"Dad, watch how many keep-ups I can do!" "Dad, count how many times I can putt into a glass!" "Dad, time how long I can balance a golf club on my head!"

As repayment for having to provide an oversupply of parental attention, I eventually found ways to selfishly harness this compulsive energy of his, by devising several rather seedily constructed challenges for him to overcome.

While watching television together, I'd say, "Hey Boy, I'll bet you couldn't get upstairs to the cupboard and back with a bag of cookies in less than fifteen seconds flat!"

"Oh ya!" He'd enthusiastically announce while springing to his feet.

"Ok then, on your marks, get set, go!"

And once he broke from the starting blocks I would begin counting out loud, "One, two, three," then return to watching my program until I heard him rebounding back down the stairs. "Thirteen, fourteen," then stopping the clock one second before his arrival. "Awesome!" I'd shout out while congratulating and high fiving him— until a few minutes later when I required a glass of milk to go with my cookies.

Surprisingly, Talon never quite outgrew his childhood obsession. No doubt myself likely in part to blame for that, as so entertained was I by his habitual harlequinades that I continued to encourage him well into manhood. To put it another way, should Diane and I be out shopping, for example, and incidentally pass by a shelf of novelty games like paddle ball or the one with a cup on a stick attached to a ball and string, I'd toss them into the cart.

"Why are you getting these?" Diane would curiously question me.

"Talon is coming up this weekend." —nonchalantly answering back, causing her to smile and shake her head.

When I felt the moment was right, and he looked particularly indisposed, I'd paddle-ball past him proclaiming, "Look Tal, I can do this twenty-nine times in a row without fail!"

Predictably, and to my utter amusement, he'd say, "Gimme that, twenty-nine times, that's easy!"

Three or four hours later, he could still be heard somewhere about the house determinedly counting up, "Fifty-seven, fifty-eight, fifty-nine..."

In Zahra, Talon soon found his own perfect patsy to pass on the family tradition, as she too could spend hours unweariedly participating in whatever challenges he had thought up for her. And indisputably, it was his desire for Kitten to become proficient in the art of table tennis, which eventually consumed so much of their precious time together.

Setting Zahra up at one end of the table, he began by getting her to swat at the ball. Advancing the training, she soon mastered returning it with some degree of accuracy towards him. And after several weekends of reorienting and reinstructing, Talon had managed, with considerable diligence, to convey to Kitten the concept of knocking the ball back over the net. From here on in, it was game on!

"Mom, Dad!" He'd shout up from the bottom of the stairs. "You won't believe it, seven times!"

Selfishly seizing the opportunity, I'd yell back down to him, "Bet you'll never get ten out of her Boy."

When it came time for time with Heidi, Zahra found a welcome respite from all the racketing and gaming by joining in and doing with Heidi what Heidi did best when blessing us with a visit—curling up and squirreling away beneath the covers with a good book. For prolonged periods of the day we hardly saw neither hide nor hair of them, concerningly causing Diane to at some point call out, "Martin, can you go and check to see if they are alive in there, and if they are find out if they would like a snack."

I'd tap quietly on the bedroom door, easing it open only to see Max at the foot of the bed and Zahra wrapped and snuggled up on Heid's lap, listening as she quietly read out the passages on the pages in front of them.

"How's it going?" I'd whisper.

"Good, she loves crime stories"

"Really Heidi?" Tossing in a look of disbelief.

"Ya dad, *like* if I stop reading, she gets *like* frustrated, and then *like* starts pattering at the pages!" —came bounding the philosophically well-articulated declaration from our over- educated psychotherapist.

And for every time I have read or heard someone claiming that "there is nothing better than to have a doctor or lawyer in the family," I can say from experience and with absolute certainty, that of no lesser value is the benefit of having a mechanic in the family!

Beneath all her thorns and prickles, Karly genuinely had the kindest of hearts, and as such, she would freely offer her mechanical services, less parts and presents of course, to not only her parents, siblings and Joanna, but for all her grams, gramps and cousins as well.

So invaluable had Karly's expertise become to all of us that she quickly and easily moved to the top of the speed dial list for the entire clan. However, it must be said that her patience was indeed very often tested, particularly whenever one of us would on occasion, interrupt her busy day with an over-the-phone featherbrained enquiry. The gold medal award going to her cousin Kevin, a doctor no less, who working in the emergency room and making life or death decisions, had one day sent Karly a photo of his car's front tire to enquire if she thought it might need a dose of air?

Barring the ludicrous or laughable, should the job require a hoist or heavy tools, Karly would have each one of us bring our vehicles after hours or on weekends to her bay at Mercedes. But more often than not, whatever it was that needed replacing or repair was usually manageable at homes or our house when she came up for Sunday visits.

For Zahra, the moment she heard an engine rumbling in the garage and caught wind of Karly slipping on her fusty oily overalls, she would come bounding through her catty door and immediately take up position right alongside her apprentice.

I'd always enjoy taking a few minutes to lean up with my arms crossed against the frame of the door between the house and the garage to watch them discussing and diagnosing beneath or out from under the hood of my Chevy pickup. And because of Karly's pocket-sized frame, this required her to place her foot onto the front bumper and hoist herself up and right beside Kitten—knees knocking together atop the radiator, their little butts' side by side, their heads and shoulders dipping and disappearing down into the cavity of the firewall, leaving behind only the soles of Karly's boots and Zahra's tail, dangling down and against the front of the grill.

Much the same was the scene whenever I found the two of them tandem straddled beneath the frame of the truck, feet and tail only sticking out while deliberating the size of the sockets.

"No, Kitten, that's a 5/16th, I think we need a half-inch," they'd jammer on as Zahra tinkered and toyed through the trays full of wrenches and ratchets.

Now, be all this as it may, no one with even the smallest amount of life experience could deny that without pain there can be no gain, for every action there is a reaction and without fail, wisdom can surely not be acquired. And so, to this, it must be said, that in spite of all of the wondrous and love inspiring acts that so endeared us to Zahra, it was her incessant and unabating nefarious infatuation with the damn lavatory that on the other hand dependably drove us nuts!

If she wasn't licking our toothbrushes or knocking them into the sink, she'd be unravelling rolls of toilet paper or knocking over and riffling through the wastebasket. Worse still, she had managed somehow to figure out that should one of us be in the shower, she could incite an outburst of holy holler by simply flushing the toilet. Of course, these dastardly deeds paled in comparison to the crown jewel of her offences, and a term that soon became synonymous with the word "yuck" in our house, "Toilet Tail"

Regardless of Diane's repetitive on-bended-knee pleas for me to "please put the lid down," being a man, I naturally would sooner or later have forgotten to do so. That being the case, in no time at all, Zahra could be faithfully found sitting princessly positioned upon the throne, and for some unfathomable reason that to this day I still can't understand, allowing her tail to dip down and into the icy-cold water of the bowl below.

Nothing, and I mean nothing was grosser than working in the kitchen or at the barbeque preparing a wonderful dinner, than having Kitten glaze past your bare leg with a splash of toilet tail!

Or so I thought!

One evening, as Diane and I had retired to bed early, unusually exhausted after having spent the day cleaning and caring for house and yard, a dispassionately unforgiving mother nature had abruptly decided, somewhere deep into the middle of the midnight hours, that perhaps I should make an unscheduled but quick-footed trip to the loo.

Still half asleep and shuffling along in the dark, I suddenly and accidentally, with that horrible and all too familiar cracking sound, stubbed and slammed my toe right into the foot of the bed— sending me hurling over, winded in agony and clinging to the bedrails so as not to fall to the floor! Cursing under my breath, to avoid disturbing her majesty, I hobbled to the bathroom, finished up my business and then slipped back onto my back under the covers to snuggle and wiggle up tight against my bedmate.

"Hunny?" In a tone as if she were addressing a kindergartner.

"What?"

"Did you remember to put the toilet lid down?"

"I don't know Hun, please, I am so tired, shush! Ok?"

ONCE THE THROBBING in my toe had finally begun to subside, I started to drift mercifully back to sleep. And just as I was teetering at the edge of peaceful unconsciousness, Zahra, on a midnight pilgrimage to god-knows-where, strolled across my chest, dragging her unspeakably disgusting and freshly wetted dripping toilet tail across my lips!

"Ugh! God damn it, Zahra, ugh, yuck, son of a bitch!"

Throwing off the blankets, I dashed in haste for the sink, smashing my knee into the bedpost along the way. "Shit!" and still in a germ panic kept hopping to the taps, cupping, scooping and splashing water onto my face—then soaping, gargling and brushing several times over, before fumbling back to bed like a wounded soldier from the battlefront!

Sitting myself down at the midpoint of the bedside, I could then feel the tattletale signs of a shaking mattress, that told me that someone nearby was hysterically laughing in silence.

"Really Diane? How could you think that was funny?"

"You're right, I'm sorry, Hun."

And as I eased myself down onto my side and pulled the covers up over my shoulder, I felt a little tap on my tush.

"But I'll bet you'll never forget to put that lid down ever again, eh?"

Chippy

By the first of June, all the wonderfully good things that had crawled out from beneath winter's heavy blanket were now in full *boom*. Blessing us with a kaleidoscope of coloured hydrangeas, rhododendrons and daylilies that filled out Diane's creatively created gardens and grounds. Unfortunately to that came also the less desirable. Not the least of which was an abundance of mosquitos, black flies and in our little corner of the world, an oversupply of badly behaved chipmunks.

Cute as the dickens, I would have had no qualms about cohabitating with the rascally rodents, be it that they did not try to get into the garage or the attic the moment the opportunity presented itself. That year, for whatever the reason, perhaps their parents had little else to do over the particularly long winter, they had plainly overstepped the populous mark— by infusing into our neighbourhood more than their fair share of citizenry. That being the case, it left me little choice but to dig out and dust off the live animal trap I stored in the shed and then get right down to the business of relocation and deportation.

Despite having the upper hand of numbers on their side, when it came to this little private turf war of ours, their one inherent weakness, and my ace in the hole, was that the little buggers were easy to apprehend — once they'd caught a whiff and dab of peanut butter on toast that is. A crafty creation that was as irresistible to our prankish pals, as a steaming hot fresh slice of pepperoni pizza was to me or a chocolate-cherry love blizzard with extra chunks of turtles was to my Diane.

And Zahra, fettered with feline instincts, was as such predictably and understandably, hands-down, the *Catch and Release Program's* biggest fan and devotee! Championing the cause with irrepressible passion and zeal, she would insist on being an active participant throughout the entire operation. In fact, once Kitten had fully conceptualized the logistics of what it was that we were actually doing, she would help facilitate success by designating the right spot and then circling the trap several times to ensure the bountiful bait was perfectly placed behind the lever.

So much so that on one particular occasion, shortly after having set up the trap, and presumably not particularly pleased with the placement of bribery, she had wiggled herself into apparatus and while adjusting the bait triggered down the door behind her. Wondering suddenly where the hell she had gotten off to, I began frantically searching the grounds, only to discover poor Kitten wedge-locked and immobilized, meowing out for help from inside the cage!

Notwithstanding a slip-up or malfunction here or there, once all was set and ready the two of us would scamper back up to the house to get ourselves a snack and then take up position behind the blinds of a window—to wait and watch as yet another dupe was effectively duped.

Diane, not wanting to have any part in the whole affair, believing it to be a load of *stuff and nonsense,* insisted however, "That in no way shape or form does any harm come to the little creatures in the process, and I mean it Martin!"

Not fully appreciating her unrelenting opposition to Kitten and I poaching up a little fun and excitement together, we nonetheless continued without her support and back to the mission at hand. Hyper focused on the trap and possessing a keener eye than I, I'd know the minute a chipmunk was on final approach to the snare when Zahra began chirping and gnashing her teeth.

"Chippy? Do you see a Chippy Kitten?" I'd call out from the fridge while refilling our drinks.

Sure enough, *clink and click* would go the trap door, sending me and my mate tearing out the back door and flying down the steps of the deck and on to the trap to review and process the prisoner.

After allowing for a momentary but meaningful exchange of sniffs and sneers between, well, cat and mouse, we'd load the little gaffer carefully onto the back of my pickup truck. Surprisingly tolerant and good humoured about the whole thing, the little captive culprit, Kitten and I would soon head off to a relocation at a particular institution or a place of residence of someone of whom I'd thought deserved a *good old-fashion infestation*. *And although you didn't hear it from me,* some of my favourites were the municipal tax office, our lawyer's house or the ever-popular quarters of the snow-plough driver—who had knocked down, without concern or repair I might add, our mailbox three times that year.

Now, forasmuch as I usually respected my dear Diane's directives, I would find myself, on occasions when I felt confidently and positively sure that she was absent, succumbing to an overwhelming urge to release the little varmint, so as that Zahra might enjoy an innocent little cat and mouse chase about the yard.

Not as cruel as it sounds, as the chipmunks were quicker off the draw and nibble-footed enough to regularly avoid being Kitten captured. Once gaining their bearings, and after a short dash across the grounds, they'd speedily scamper up a tree, perch on a branch, turn and begin chipping, twitching and angrily cursing and cussing!

"Well then keep off my property and stay out of my garage!" I'd yell back up the tree at them, before affirmatively going back to the business of replacing and resetting the trap with Kitten.

One fine morning, Zahra and I had returned up to the house after setting up, when before long Kitten began chirping and gnashing her teeth at about the same time as Diane started chirping and gnashing hers.

"I'm just heading to town to run some errands, I'll be back in about an hour," she relayed while slipping on her shoes and jacket.

Then, just as the front door slammed shut behind her,

the trap door slammed shut behind yet another sucker—sending Kitten and I scurrying, scuttering and sprinting out to the backyard.

After arriving we were surprised to see not a chipmunk but rather instead an uncommonly large and robust black squirrel. As of yet not having any beefs with squirrels and fully believing that *you know who* had gone to town, I thought, well what's the harm in having a little fun, and so released the little nut-stasher out for Zahra to have after it.

Of course, I had no idea that right then and there, *you know who* had in the process returned home to retrieve her forgotten purse. And I swear by all that is good and holy, the second I opened that trap door and that squirrel went flying out with Kitten flying off after it, the back door went flying open and *you know who* started screaming!

"ARE YOU KIDDING ME!"

So unnerved, startled and stunned was I by her shriek that I quite nearly shot straight out of my shoes!

Caught red-handed *again*, and entirely at a loss for words or what to say for myself, I felt fortunate only in that at least for the moment her attention had been intensely redirected to the unfolding chase at hand.

Zigzagging around the yard, snaking, curving and twisting in and out of Diane's gardens, prey and predator continued ripping apart the flower beds and tearing up the grass for what seemed like an eternity. You know, in hindsight, if that fluffy-tailed jerk just had had the decency to hurl and hotfoot it up a tree, he'd have spared me at least to some degree the bawling out that was surely and shortly coming my way.

But, almost as if consciously and deliberately calculating a plan of pay-back, he instead willfully and with full intent made not for the forest, but rather right for the house.

Scaling up the deck post and weaving through the railing spindles, gaining precious ground on Kitten still in hot pursuit, he vaulted up onto the banister, pausing for a moment as if to consider what his next move should be.

Callously calculating he then tossed a quick glance at, my still for the time being, stone-cold frozen wife, then at the open doorway to the kitchen and then down and around to myself— still standing like a stone pillar, open-mouthed and wide-eyed staring up from the yard. Squirrelly smirking, I suddenly understood what his fiendish little mind was plotting, and so began shaking my head from side to side, pleading with him not to do it!

Needless to say, he bounded straight down onto the deck barreling right through the legs of my hysterically screaming spouse, precisely and directly into the house with Curly, Larry and Moe tagging undeviatingly on in behind.

With Kitten hot on his heels they went scampering up onto the kitchen counters knocking over tins of tea and white sugar before bounding up to the tops of the cupboards and carelessly bowling through and smashing down a line of no-longer precious dishes. Scaling then across and over to the dining table, they began rippling up the table linens while tipping into and spilling over

Diane's beautiful arrangement of dahlias onto the floor. Off to the living room they blissfully continued, leaping up and into the cabinetry and recklessly ejecting a life-time collection of CDs and sacred home movies like wood from a wood chipper.

"Martin! Not the China cabinet!"—Diane cried out for heavenly mercy, begging I hastily position myself like a defensive lineman between our family's beloved heirlooms and the rabble-rousing home wreckers hell-bent on tearing up the place limb from limb.

On and on this went, until finally, squirrel, likely running out of fuel or fun, sought sudden refuge by spring-boarding himself up from the end table lamp, half pike and full twist before rounding off securely onto a blade of the ceiling fan above. The incoming force and momentum gently propelled the fan into a slow and easy rotation—while he sat peacefully and properly atop going around and around as if being showcased at a squirrel convention for the audience of three bombed and bamboozled below.

Hands now planted firmly on her hips and donning that affectionate and loving familiar look upon her beautiful face, Diane asked of her beloved husband and lifelong soulmate,

"So what now, asshole?"

The pellet gun came to mind, but given my poor marksmanship, I would probably have ended up just maiming the little bastard and or peppering my ceiling with bullet holes.

Wracking my brain for a more peaceful solution, it

suddenly occurred to me that perhaps I might be able to fishing net the little home wrecker and so darted quickly to the garage to retrieve— promptly returning now armed and ready to receive.

No doubt the image of a fool, trying to bag a squirrel from the living room fan with a fishing net, I nonetheless, having not a better idea, slowly extended the pole towards him.

As one could expect, fearing capture, he suddenly sprang and flew, flying squirrel style formation from the fan directly for the open doorway— bridging the gap by step-stoning, I kid you not, right onto and over the very top of Diane's head!

And you know, I must say, if you've never had the opportunity of at least once in your life having seen a hysterically screaming spouse sporting a black squirrel cap, boy you've really missed something.

A Man's Business is
His Business

"**A** Picnic!" She tossed back the sheets, rolled out from the bed and into her overflowing and arguably over-elaborated silk kimono. "Don't you think that's a wonderful idea on a day like this?" Abruptly waking me from my nightmare—shipwrecked on a desert isle—castaway with a warren of Playboy Bunnies as my only source of company.

With zest and zeal, she rounded the foot of our bed, dashing to the bedroom window, grasping onto the drapery and throwing them arms-wide open. And standing there, with the boughs of her limbs cast out to the walls, the veils of her technicolour bathrobe draped to the floor and the morning sun shining down upon her beautiful face, she looked to me much like I imagined Moses must have appeared to the Israelites as he parted the Red Sea.

Twirling around to me at my bedside, she demanded, "Well, what do you think?"

Not forgetting that I had just nearly squirreled her to death, I with one eye shut and the other wincing at the beams of sunlight divinely creeping through the locks of her strawberry blonde hair, rather humbly replied, "Um, ya, a picnic, ok, sure, where?"

Bursting with epiphany, she snapped and pointed her finger at me. "The pond, I'll set up some chairs, pack us a lunch, while you two," patting Kitten on the top of her head, "can fish for trout and I can catch up on my reading."

"Picnic basket, picnic basket," rapping her forefinger upon her lips, "Where did I put that damn picnic basket?" Then with a sudden revelation she charged out from our bedchamber, raving and rankling through the halls full of closets until some minutes later, as if having unearthed a precious jewel, exuberantly announced, "Ha-ha, I found it!"

Quickly returning and plunking herself down at the side of the bed with the basket upon her lap she lovingly proclaimed, "Martin look, isn't it beautiful!"—running her hands lovingly across the edges and down the sides of the intricately interwoven strands of tawny wicker.

"Ya, very nice, where did you get it?"

"Where did I get it you jerk— you gave it to me for our anniversary a few years ago."

While strangely having no particular recollection of this, I nonetheless watched with some interest as she slowly and carefully opened the lid, as if it were an enormous jewelry box cradling yet another diamond ring.

From within emerged a red and white checkered lining that provided a quaint and charming backdrop for several rows of leather bindings—neatly holding in place two sets of silver cutlery, a pair of elegant wine glasses and a small stack of porcelain crockery. Zahra, standing with her front paws on the ridges of my hips and curiously careening her neck to see what was inside, naturally did what every cat does when presented with the opportunity of an opened box or bag, she bounded straight in.

"Ha ha," Diane laughed, commencing immediately into several repetitious renditions of Pop Goes the Weasel while simultaneously turning an imaginary handle— giggling and lifting the lid as little Bengal in the box popped her silly head out.

"Really Diane?"

"Listen, why don't we," brushing the hair away from the front of my eyes, "get cleaned up and while you and Zahra dig out our rods and tackle, I'll run to town to get the stuff for salmon and egg salad sandwiches."

Once our morning affairs were all in order, Diane made like a flash for town, while Kitten and I, somewhat less enthusiastically, climbed and clambered up to the rafters of the garage to retrieve our cobb webbed and dusty gear.

Mission quickly accomplished, I suddenly found myself in a moment of quiet with nothing particularly important to do, and so after having sent Diane a message reminding her to pick up a box of red wigglers at the bait shop, I decided that perhaps now would be a good time to make a precautionary pre-field trip visit to the latrine.

Now, whether it be by divine creation or natural design, the simple fact of the matter is that a man's business is his business—and much to our beloved counterpart's frequent bewilderment, it is a solemn duty that requires of us not only time and patience, but above of all a period of undisturbed privacy.

Precisely why, as I sat down to business that morning, I was fair to say *alarmingly unsettled* when a loud *thunk* and a pair of paws came jetting out from beneath the crack of the doorway—as if some little caped crusading feline super-hero had accidentally flown herself headfirst into the outside of the bathroom door.

"Zahra go away!" I steely insisted. But Kitten, clearly not having any plans of entertaining that notion, began rather to tap and patter her paws feverishly back and forth along the tiles—much like a mad pianist banging out a concerto on the keys of a grand piano.

Then suddenly, dangling a wisp of hope that she'd thankfully found something better to entertain herself with, she promptly retreated and retracted her paws. As one might expect, a foolish presumption, as in actuality she'd only needed a moment to realign her guns— flipping over onto her back, inverting and then reinserting her mauls, claws to the ceiling, now raking at the base of the door. As she continued to clank, clatter and batter at the hatch, I came to a bloodcurdling horrific realization that, in my haste for the throne, I had made the dreadful and unthinkable error of improperly securing the latch.

Like the calm before a storm, all unexpectedly then went quiet.

You know, just the way she kicked that door wide open, *Shining- Style,* and then just sat there staring me down with that diabolical Cheshire grin on her fiendish little face, I had absolutely no reservations that I was now once again in deep, deep yogurt!

"Zahra buzz off! I began to order and plead with her—

which as anticipated, only served to strengthen her resolve to make the most out of my precariously vulnerable position.

Fully realizing that all hell was soon to break loose, I began wretchedly considering what if any defensive countermeasures I might have at my disposal. Stupidly, I thought that if I tore off sheets of toilet tissue, rolled them into little balls and finger-flung them over her head and into the hallway, she'd decamp and vamoose after them.

But like a poor marksman, I more often than not completely missed the target—landing a higher percentage of salvos into the bathtub, onto the counter or even bouncing off the top Kitten's head.

Disconcertingly I eventually ran the supply of tissue ammunition down to the end of the roll—leaving me no choice but to initiate a *last-ditch Hail Mary* empty toilet roll spiral to the far reaches of the hallway, hoping it might distract her attention long enough for me to finish up and get the hell out of there.

Not a chance!

Leading the offensive charge, she vaulted up onto the counter- top, pausing only for a moment to survey the theatre of operations while sniffing and swatting at the bonsai tree and Diane's cluster full of white orchids, before then advancing on to a tinkling of the taps and an incidental spilling of our toothbrushes into the sink.

Creeping ever nearer to my side, I began to angrily warn her, "Zahra, I'm not kidding leave me alone!" But no sooner had I spoke my last syllable than did she spring to the edge of the window sill, and in the process, dislodged the painting on the wall behind me—sending it careening straight razor shave down the length of my back, the frame now wedged firmly between the back of the seat and the cheeks of my buttocks!

"Ahhhhhhhhhhh!" I howled out in agonizing pain! "Zahra, God damn it!"

Having now had enough, I reached to my side to retract from the basket the last roll of loo paper and began, in a fluster, fidgeting to get it back onto the rack. Chaos Kitten, now seizing upon the chance to advance her rank, quickly jumped from the sill to the floor and in one fell swoop, batted the roll from my grip, sending it, as the two of us watched, unspooling across the breadth of the bathroom floor!

In synchronicity, our heads turned back to face each other as if only to exchange a quick but meaningful glance. Mine, begging her to please not abscond with the last of the bathroom tissue, and hers, conveying in return, but only one word, "*Sucker!*"

Springing full-appendage-sprawl into the air and pouncing down onto the lane of paper, she madly mono-rail- army-crawled her way out and down the line with shredded tissue shrapnel flying everywhere until stopping only at the end of the roll, now tipping and teetering at the top of the staircase.

At that point, she sat up and began to long-stare me down—still royally seated and gleaming back at her while shaking my finger and warning, "Zahra, don't you dare!"

Without a blink or breaking her stare, she just tapped the remnants of roll, sending it bouncing and unravelling down the stairs, with her, of course, triumphantly chasing after it.

"For heaven's sake, I can't believe this," grumbling to myself, before noticing that a half-dozen or so tears of tissue broken off in the attack, had become statically stuck to the frame of the door. In a state of paperless panic and fearing the slightest dust of wind might send them flying away, I jumped to my feet, entirely forgetting in the process that I was still trouser bound at the ankles.

Now timbering forward, I desperately tried to counteract the force of gravity by flailing my arms and doddering my heels—but to little avail— for as I did the humiliating *penguin shuffle* while shouting for help I tripped like a fool at the lip of the door that then sent me crashing face-first down onto the floor.

At that very moment, *Mrs. Picnic* came blasting into the house, jowls wagging as she surveyed the damage. Stepping carefully forward and looking down upon her poor husband, face planted, bare butt and hogtied, she assertively demanded— "Martin, what the hell are you doing?"

With a modicum of sarcasm, I cracked my neck up towards her standing there above me and calmly replied, "I'm fishing for lake trout, what does it look like I am doing?"

Mathew's Mayhem

The first time Diane and I met, quite by chance as things providential often seem to be, we were all of but 15 and 14 years old, respectively. She was a hard-working beautiful young girl, earning summer dollars by lifeguarding at community pools in our hometown of Streetsville, Ontario—where I on the other hand was your typical up-to-no-good Levi's and leather, long live rock and roll troublemaker. Luckily for me however that had a certain appeal, and after our paths had serendipitously crossed, we spent the rest of that summer "*going around*" together.

Undeniably not the kind of fella you'd want your young daughter going out with, I even had the audacity in those days to frequently steal my mother's keys and etch the car out of the drive just so that I could take Diane joyriding. Whenever I think back now to the two of us, barely able to see over the dashboard, dusting down some country road together, I always shake my head and shutter in unbelief.

Unfortunately, because of the turbulence within my family and of course my own rebellious nature, I was sent that fall to live with my father and his new wife, Renate. As I was now in a new town and new school, Diane and I sadly but quickly drifted apart and would not see nor speak to each other again until an even more unlikely encounter some eight years later.

Those years in between were particularly difficult for me. Being from different generations and cultures, my father and I hardly saw eye-to-eye and whatever relationship we did have was more often than not combative. Confused and angry, it was not surprising that I had little interest in education, and so by the time I was sixteen I had been promptly expelled from not only high school but also from home.

Stubborn as I was, I spent the better part of the next six months as a penniless vagrant, sleeping in stairwells, park benches or on a good night a friend's house. Eventually though, but not without significant troubles, I managed to refocus my life on becoming a musician, while dredging my way through a seemingly endless series of unsatisfying jobs, residences, and relationships.

Until the ripe old age of twenty-three that is, when an acquaintance of mine insisted one night that I accompany him to a new club in Toronto where there, auspiciously was Diane. Just twenty- two, unattached, still living with mom and dad, and like me wondering how the hell the stars had managed so impossibly to leave us once again standing at the crossroads together.

Admittedly awestruck, dazed and even a little confused, as to how the image in my mind of the short-haired, redheaded little girl I used to pal around with had stunningly transformed into the drop-dead gorgeous bombshell now standing before me. For myself at least, it was love at first sight, and having spent eight long battle-hardened years in the trenches of life, I can tell you I was more than ready to lasso this little filly.

That night we talked for hours about old times, how we'd gotten to where we were and me filling her head with all my crazy ideas about the future, the things I wanted to do and the places I wanted to see. In retrospect, I must have done a pretty good job of strutting my feathers, because a whirlwind romance quickly ensued and by the end of the following year we were married.

The problem for me soon after that was that despite a good song and dance, I really had little to offer Diane in the way of a secure future. With no education, no money, our first child now on the way and only a string of dead-end jobs to show for, I was to Diane's frustration, too often down in the dumps about it.

We'd frequently talk about this sitting around the dining room card table in the leaky and musty hovel with skunks under the floor and squirrels in the attic that we'd rented. And being the supportive person that Diane always was, she eventually, though rather offhandedly, suggested that perhaps I should go back to school and get a career.

"Like what?" I remember asking.

"Well, you are really good with children, maybe a teacher? Besides, the benefits are good, and we would have summers to do things together?"

Tantalizing as the notion was to me, the road from *here*

to there seemed impossible. I hadn't even a high school education and with mouths to feed and bills to pay the mountain was clearly and plainly just too high.

Nevertheless, the scheme had a carrot for sure, and for weeks it refused to stop niggling around in my noodle. Eventually, the two of us decided to make the short trek up to the nearby University of Guelph, to query what if any possibilities they might have to offer. To our surprise, it turned out that I was eligible for the Mature Student Program. A probationary semester that, if completed with satisfactory grades, would lead to full-time undergraduate study, a bachelor's degree, and eligibility for the one-year Elementary Teacher licensing course at Toronto's York University.

As simple as that, with Diane taking on two jobs, me delivering pizza and driving trucks part-time, and our parents helping with the arrival and care of babies two and three, we managed over the next four and a half years to acquire not only a teaching degree, but an enlarged family, and regrettably, a whopping load of financial debt as well!

By the fall of 1997 I was finally primed and ready to start teaching and earning money. Unfortunately, a shrinking job market coupled to an unprecedented oversupply of recent graduates soon made finding work exceedingly difficult. Eventually, I felt compelled to take a position in a remote fly-in First Nations Community on the shores of Lake Athabasca— far in the reaches of Northern Saskatchewan and only a stone's throw away from the border of the North West Territories.

Despite the apparent challenges this presented us, with a young family and all, the pay was good, our expenses were covered, and most importantly I'd have my foot in the door.

And so, with our parents scratching their heads in shock and awe, the five of us and a year's worth of luggage set off by train that September from Toronto's Union Station bound for Saskatoon.

To our amazement, it required nearly three days to traverse only a part of the immense expanse of geography that is Canada. Three days, that is, of back-breaking sleeps, children screaming and running up and down the aisles and little else to do but admire the scenery passing by.

A memorable experience, nonetheless, we finally arrived in Saskatoon and proceeded immediately to the local grocery store to complete the second phase of our journey— boxing up and mailing to ourselves three months' worth of supplies. This entailed if I remember correctly, packaging and posting thirteen carriages full of non-perishable goods that included, but were not limited to, toiletries, cereal, and canned beans.

The next leg of our trip required two connecting flights, the first from Saskatoon to La Ronge and then from there onto the outpost of Fond du Lac. Diane, who at the time, wasn't too keen on small aircraft, managed the first part in a newer twin turbo- prop with only marginal anxiety. However, she literally needed to be pushed into the next, a 1956 Twin Otter retrofitted with school bus seats, a lumberjack-jacket clad pilot, his golden retriever and all of our baggage under straps of rope netting at the back of the plane.

As a matter of course we eventually made it to the airfield, where we were welcomed by several of the Dene Band's elders, the school principal and three Royal Canadian Mounted Police— who proceeded to search our bags for illegal alcohol banned in the community—which I may or may not now admit was cleverly concealed by Diane as wrapped birthday gifts for our children. In any case, we had arrived safely and soon settled into our new accommodations alongside an eclectic mix of other teachers from all parts of the country.

That school year that we lived and worked amongst the Dene people, we inherited an entire novels' worth of experiences and memories. But suffice to say, we made many new friends and colleagues and learned much about the culture, language and troubles of the First Nations people that live in such remote places of the country. We angled for the northern sharks that grow enormous in the waters of Athabasca, learned how to filet and make Bannock, snowmobiled across frozen lakes to other communities and hunted for caribou— and over time managed to make a difference in the lives of many of my students, some of whom still after so many years stay in touch with me today.

The following spring, all the wiser, we headed for home and to an exciting new opportunity for me as a Special Education teacher at a public Elementary School in nearby Brampton, Ontario.

It was precisely here that very soon an unexpected

series of events would begin to unfold that would change all our lives dramatically and forever.

Section 23, as it was then called, was in this case a satellite program in a regular host school for a maximum of eight identified high-risk behavioural students—each of whom always arrived with not only unbalanced emotions and violent tempers, but a sack full of family baggage that was more often than not the root cause of their afflictions.

My interest in the field naturally stemmed from wanting to help kids that had suffered difficult childhoods like myself. Owing to additional qualifications in Behaviour, my recent experience in Fond du Lac, the fact that the current incumbent had finally had enough and that most likely no one else wanted the position anyway, the principal felt that I was now the right man for the job.

Along with my faithful teaching assistant Ann Brown, a fully padded timeout room and an emergency hotline, we'd set off that first year to make as much difference in our students' tumultuous lives as possible.

As basic as it may have seemed, I planned to encourage good behaviour by modifying and simplifying the academics to functional language and mathematics only and granting rewards if the children managed to complete their daily assignments without killing each other in the process. Specifically, in addition to regular outings to the YMCA for my kids, I offered to run lunch-time intramural sports for the entire school—this so as that I could integrate my own students mainstream, in a fun and healthy activity that for safety reasons I was able to supervise directly.

Given the green light by the administration, I chose to organize indoor soccer—partly because of my personal interests in the sport and partly because over the previous several years, Diane and I had gained considerable experience managing and coaching our son Talon's house league team.

With our program in place, Ann and I began the task of managing a collection of hard-luck cases whose personal stories too often wrenched at our heartstrings as a result of the terrible experiences they'd only thus far had to endure. On the upside, our classroom environment soon provided not only a daily safe reprieve from their troubles at home, but in a way some hope for the future as well.

For whatever the reasons, innate, environment or likely some combination of both, we found as we began to know them, each had been blessed with the most outlandish personalities.

And of all the souls that came into our classroom that year, it was undoubtedly Mathew that most often had Ann and I shaking our heads in wonder.

While both myself and my trusted assistant were firmly opposed to the overprescribing of medication as a way to control the children's behaviour, Mathew, on the other hand, it could be said was a poster child for Ritalin if there ever was one. The poor kid simply could not control his motor, which ran continually at full RPM and infuriatingly had no off switch! Adversely, while on his meds, Mathew could sit quietly without distraction and focus on his assignments for hours at a time. Of course the problem for us and for Mathew's nearly depleted grandmother, who had been given sole charge of him by the courts until his mother got her act together, was that he would routinely try, at all costs, to avoid taking his daily medication as he was supposed to.

A baby-faced, stout and stocky, four-foot-nothing ten-year-old, it took us only nanoseconds to realize whenever he had arrived yet again *uncaged*—eventually requiring that we keep a stockpile of pills at school to ensure he ultimately settled into a manageable disposition. It went without saying that his frail and exhausted grandmother was hardly to blame, as she had little means to deal with Mathew and was too often at her wit's end just trying to manage the situation.

Despite all of his chest pounding and saber-rattling tactics, we soon realized that deep down inside, Mathew was at heart just a big baby. And never was this more apparent than one afternoon late that fall when his Nanna unexpectedly arrived, visibly distraught, at the classroom door.

Out in the quiet of the hallway, she began to explain that without Mathew's medication he was challenging to handle—I heard that—but because he refused to take an intermittent blood test, his doctor was unable to renew his much needed prescriptions.

"Why won't Mathew take a blood test," I asked somewhat confused.

"Mathew afraid of needle," she replied in a slight Portuguese accent while shaking her head and rolling back her eyes. Trying to contain my laughter, I asked how I could help.

"Please," while placing her hand affectionately upon my arm, "Please, for me, please take Mathew to doctor office today, please."

Sincerely wanting to help, and without a doubt having ourselves a vested interest in the mission, I assured her that come hell or high water I'd get it done. Ann, always the faithful trooper, thankfully agreed to help with the project— so as the final bell for the day rang it was now time for *Operation Lifelabs!*

Mathew's suspicions that something was seriously wrong began to hit home soon after I had excused his classmates for the day—leaving him alone and nervously wondering why Ann had moved into position in front of the doorway and I was rolling up my sleeves.

"Mathew!" I demanded in a father-like tone, "It's time to give a little blood."

"No, no! Please no," tears streaming down his face, "Please, Mr. S, don't do this to me! I'm going to die!"

"Mathew you big baby, everyone does it all the time it won't hurt you,"—I tried to console him, naively believing that he might still be reasoned into peaceful cooperation.

However, the futility of trying to successfully negotiate with a *frenzied neurotic* soon became apparent. And Mathew, realizing that I was now preparing to handle him physically, panic- stricken, committed himself to a series of ridiculous escape maneuvers by hurdling over desks and scurrying under tables.

Once or twice I had him by the feet, but he managed to squirm and squiggle loose, taking again to fleeing like a lunatic about the classroom. After a considerable amount of time and energy pursuing him, the two of us finally had him cornered—where to our utter disbelief he made a desperate last-ditch Hail Mary dive for the half-open window—inadvertently wedging his pudgy little body partway in and partway out, frantically kicking his feet and hoping to jiggle himself loose and away to freedom.

Before that could happen Ann and I had quickly gotten hold of him by his legs and we were doing our best to yank and haul the little ninny back into the room. Yet no matter how hard we pulled, he resolutely and obstinately refused to dislodge from the window casement.

Eventually, we realized that he had grasped onto the branch of a hedge just outside the building, and obviously so, because each time we had at him, the hedge would correspondingly shake vigorously. Boy oh boy, as the tug of war raged on, I began to envision the astounded faces of the parents, students and staff outside still waiting for the arrival of busses—no doubt watching in horror as Mathew, clutching, screaming and pleading for his life, was now slowly but steadily being pulled back inside.

Suddenly the branch gave way and snapped loose sending the three of us and a good portion of the hedge hurtling backward onto the classroom floor. And if I thought we'd finally got the better of him, I would have been clearly mistaken, as he rebounded almost instantaneously, flogging twigs and leaves at me in a bid to buy time and once again have for the open window.

"Oh no you don't," I countered, clasping him by the belt loop of his knickers while drawing on his fleeting energy to pull myself up and onto my feet. Now desperately trying to restrain and contain him with his fists flailing about wildly, Ann began to plead with him.

"Mathew! Mathew, we are not going to let anyone hurt you!"

But Mathew wanted no part of it, instead diverting all his remaining energy into screaming bloody blue murder at near ear-bleeding decibels.

Ann, entirely frustrated and finally having had enough, cried out in her staunch Liverpudian accent, "Right, that's it! You've got the arms, I've got the legs, let's go!" And with that, we levitated him up by his four appendages and promptly made our way down the hall to the parking lot door—poor Mathew hollering and his midsection hula hooping the all the way.

Getting him out of the school and into the open door of Ann's van came easier than expected, although I supposed by now that even he needed some respite from the battle, if for nothing else but to regroup and prepare himself for what was coming next. Thankfully, the lab was only a few blocks away, offering no spare time or real opportunity for Mathew to fully refuel his tanks. Thank goodness too, because if we thought getting him to and into the van was something, getting him out would have been otherwise no less than impossible.

With his feet hooked under the front seats, his arms and hands bear-hugging the headrests and his teeth lock-jawed to the seat belts, we were entirely confounded as to how to pry him loose without possibly having to make another no less harrowing trip to the dentist's office. Then, from a generation endowed with practical sense, Ann soon came up with the simple and obvious solution

—"*tickle him!*" Worked like a charm!

Quickly we wrapped him up as before, made our way down a flight of steps and into the medical lab, which was predictably packed and stacked to the ceiling with a waiting room full of patients entirely aghast at what was now transpiring before them.

Putting on a real show for the stunned crowd of spectators, we nevertheless managed him to the registration desk, where the nurse, who had long since been notified by Mathew's grandmother of our situation, promptly and with haste shuttled us into the treatment room.

Realizing the end was near, Mathew now shifted into survival mode. With every ounce of his remaining energy, he began struggling, screaming and yelling with such ferocity that it required not only myself, Ann and the nurse, but two more lab technicians to securely hold him down long enough to finally draw out two vials of his precious blood.

And so rooted was he in his own theatrical performance that he hadn't even realized that the dirty deed was done.

"Mathew, it's over!" I repeatedly tried to convince him. "Mathew, it's over," I argued several more times, until he ultimately came around, inspected his arm, smiled ever so happily, jumped down from the table, dusted off his knees, turned to us and announced,

"Well, that wasn't so bad, eh?"

With that comment he was lucky I managed to restrain myself from giving him a real need for a doctor. Yet worse still was having to watch as he pranced out and into the waiting room, proud as a peacock, to no less than a chorus of applause and a standing ovation from everyone there.

And I kid you not, the little bugger actually took a bow!

The Family Business

One day, some months later, as I was dragging a bag of soccer balls into the gymnasium, a fellow staff member, fully aware of my passion for the sport, offhandedly asked, "Hey, what do you think of the new indoor soccer facility?"

Blindsided, perplexed and bewildered that I'd somehow missed the meeting on this, at the time, exceptionally rare development, I humbly asked for more information. She went on to explain that a Brampton based soccer club had managed to finance the conversion of an older local hockey arena into a soccer facility, by removing the boards and flooring and replacing it with an artificial grass playing field. Speechless, yet overwhelmingly intrigued, I proceeded immediately after dismissal that day to see firsthand and for myself the new Ken Giles Indoor Soccer Centre.

Regrettably, the facility was not yet fully operational nor open to the public. However, the custodian, fortuitously a soccer fanatic himself and thereby sympathetic to my enthusiasm, kindly offered to give me a sneak preview. So taken was I by the smell of fresh paint and the fluorescent lights illuminating the brilliant whites and greens of the artificial field, that I could hardly wait to get home and tell Diane all about it.

That evening, once we'd juggled and wrestled the children into bed, we poured ourselves a glass of wine and talked endlessly about how this happened and how we could utilize the center for our son Talon's team?

Hardly able to sleep that night, I awoke early the next morning and eagerly went about trying to find information on rental rates and availability at the new facility. But to my astonishment and utter disappointment, the whole place had long since been fully booked out and had in fact attracted a lengthy waiting list of other clubs and teams wanting to train players and run their own leagues.

As a result, we were forced that winter to practice and play in small elementary school gymnasiums, that for me was akin to oaring a rowboat after having toured a million-dollar yacht.

But you know this thing had a bullet and the concept so captivated my imagination that I would think about it for days and nights at a time. Not long after that, what began as merely considering ways to replicate or duplicate space to play, soon ignited in me an entrepreneurial spirit with bigger ideas on how we might just cash in on this whole indoor soccer thing.

But how?

Forget that fact that we had no business experience at all, the simple truth of the matter was that with three mouths to feed and a mound of student loans to repay, we were flat broke. Between Diane's part-time income and my entry-level teacher's salary, we often found ourselves having to return bottle deposits to the store just to put gas in the car—never mind leasing or constructing commercial buildings and outfitting them with hundreds of thousands of dollars' worth of artificial turf and sports equipment. Boy, if we thought getting an education was a mountain too high to climb, this crazy idea was no less than flying to the moon.

Of course, where there is a will there is a way, right?

GIVEN what we knew about the inner financial workings of youth and adult soccer registrations, and after much brainstorming on the matter, we eventually came up with a game plan, that with a little luck, just might work.

It went something like this:

Soccer organizations and facilities registered players and field space, in general, twice a year—in the spring for summer leagues and in the fall for winter—with the full balance of all due in full at the beginning of the season. This left the registrar sitting on a heap of operating capital and profits well in advance of the bi-annual start-up. With the obvious demand for space, alongside significant immigration to the Greater Toronto Area and a growing interest in the sport, we figured that it was mathematically possible to register enough kids, adults and clubs to adequately pay for the playing surface and the lease of a building to put it in—essentially starting a high return profitable business with no money of our own in!

Armed with this absurd and unlikely to succeed plan of ours, we nevertheless enthusiastically went about pouring over commercial real estate listings, identifying potential candidates and making appointments to see them—the absolute requirement for each having a large enough clear span area for playing soccer, or more specifically, no posts or pillars.

For months we searched high and low, but eventually and regrettably came to understand that such an animal just didn't exist. The reason being that the high cost of constructing clear span engineered buildings was so expensive that those that existed were already pre-built or in use for a specific purpose. With that knowledge, our hopes and dreams crashed to the ground and our nutty idea was shelved indefinitely.

That is until only a few weeks later, when one fateful day while on my way home from work, I decided for no specific reason to turn into the Brampton Fairgrounds Agricultural Centre to have a closer look at their large exhibit pavilion. Even though I had passed by a thousand times before, I always assumed the arena was filled with livestock, stalls, and of course pillars, so never gave it a second thought.

Wow talk about a *needle in the haystack!* I quite nearly fell over backwards after peering in through the window of a side door only to find exactly what we'd been looking for. *How could this be!?* I said to myself. Only minutes from our house, perched at the edge of the city, a massive clear span and pressed concrete-floored vacant arena—not possible!

Trying not to get too excited, I immediately proceeded

to the office building to find out if it could be rented. The manager, who recognized me from my school where her daughter attended, informed me that "Yes, we rent the arena out after the annual Fall Fair in September and currently we don't have any other tenants. What do you want it for?" she curiously then asked me.

I went on to enthusiastically describe the problems of our soccer community with respect to available space—explaining how we could put down a removable playing surface that we could store away in the off season. From there, I went on to reason that it would provide the fairgrounds with annual revenue while offering our soccer patrons a great space to play. After thinking about it for a moment, she suggested that I draw up a proposal that she would put on the executives agenda that we could present to the board members at the weekly meeting the following Wednesday for their consideration.

Well, holy crap, I nearly wet my shorts!

Entirely beside myself, I raced home and before having a chance to explain, tossed Diane and the kids into the car and flew back to the fairgrounds to show everyone, incredibly, what I had found!

Sailing now into uncharted waters and certainly out of our element, my conceivably soon-to-be business partner and I nevertheless did our best to construct a proposal outlining the details of our plan. Barren of funds, however, as in those days that we usually were, I was becoming increasingly apprehensive about entering into a significant financial commitment without any monetary means or even a whisper of legal advice.

. . .

FACE-TO-FACE with our idea potentially becoming a reality, I unconsciously began pacing back and forth, nervously muttering to myself behind Diane as she feverishly typed away. Ever the consummate optimist and having little doubts that this sucker was gonna cruise to the stars, she would intermittently shout out while shaking her head back and forth, "Get a grip Hun, this is gonna be awesome!"

Reminding myself over and again that *"history only remembers those who persist and succeed,"* we pressed on throughout the night and by the early reaches of the morning had managed through not only two bottles of red wine, but a draft proposal that even I thought wasn't half bad.

In it we detailed the hours of operation and the specifics of the removable playing surface—which consisted of a dozen large coils of artificial turf that could be rolled out, velcroed together at the seams and then reversed for removal—not forgetting, of course, the terms of a ten-year lease and *special request* for a bargain-basement rental rate—as in all likelihood, that despite whatever we told ourselves, this hair-brained scheme had a decent chance of tanking right from the get-go!

With a sample piece of artificial turf sent from our contact in Georgia, the epicenter of carpet manufacturing for all of North America, and our offer in triplicate, we set off that that following Wednesday with Diane in heels and me in jacket and tie to meet with the Agricultural Society's board of directors.

They just loved it! In fact, the vote was unanimously in favour of having indoor soccer fill the arena during the fall and winter months. Effectively attracting not only people and revenue to the Agricultural Center, but also providing the community with an invaluable recreational resource. And before you could say, "Oh boy, now we're in it up to our eyeballs," we were heading back home wondering, *what the hell had we just gotten ourselves into.*

Fully understanding that wanting something and actually having it are two entirely different creatures, I soon found myself treading about the house wringing my hands and incessantly worrying that we were way in over our heads. I mean not only had I put the two of us on the hook for a ten year commercial lease and a quarter of a million dollars' worth of plastic grass, but my in-laws as well, of whom we had to borrow ten percent of that amount just to begin production!

Thank goodness for Diane's unshakable nerve and unwavering belief that this was our ticket out of poverty, which decisively kept me from backpedaling us out of an opportunity that would soon prove to become even more than we had ever hoped for.

Throughout the spring and summer months we diligently began preparing for our grand opening in September. While Diane and the kids were busy painting road signs and designing flyers for distribution in the schools, I was meeting with soccer club officials regarding rental space and canvasing the outdoor adult leagues to extoll the virtues of playing at the new and larger indoor facility.

Once word had fully gotten out, it went viral, and the response, even to Diane's surprise, was overwhelming in the extreme. Clubs, organizations, and individuals began beating a path to our doorway, throwing fistfuls of dollars at us, all hoping to nail down the best days and hours of rental times for their leagues and programs.

On one memorable occasion, the president of the Brampton Girls' Club arrived, somewhat to my embarrassment at our broken-down shanty, with a signed rental contract and a cheque for fifty thousand dollars. Just a nobody schoolteacher with little or no business experience, I was at a loss to comprehend and deal with this sudden influx of significant capital— which was as foreign to me as terms like receivables, incorporations, and capital gains!

At any rate, by the time we had rolled out the field, painted the lines and assembled the equipment that fall, we had registered over six hundred youth players, three divisions of adult teams and hourly rentals that had us booked and sold out until midnight every day of the week.

Overnight our lives transformed, as our world effectively now became the *family business*. So much so in fact, that Diane needed to quit her day job, and I had resigned myself to being put on the teacher's supply list.

Behind the scenes, my beloved partner in crime soon became inundated with the mountainous task of administrating the whole affair—scheduling players and teams, ordering uniforms and awards, hiring and training referees and volunteers—where I on the other hand, relegated to the front lines, was given the less than desirable task of managing the day-to-day in-person operations of the arena, or as I quickly came to think of it as the *Madhouse*.

Honest to God, I don't know what it is about soccer that brings out the hooligan in people. Perhaps it's the international and multi-ethnic passions for the sport, but whatever the case, I'll tell you that even the most notoriously misbehaved hockey parents had absolutely nothing whatsoever on this lot of *crazies*.

It wasn't long before I became the go-to man on the field whenever a confrontation broke out about something, more often than not entirely ridiculous by any otherwise rational or civilized comprehension of humanity. In fact, so regularly did screaming, yelling, and fighting amongst the patrons occur that the staff sergeant at the local police detachment and myself were shortly on a first-name basis.

All kidding aside, even at the preschool level, I could be seen along with my referees breaking up fistfights between mothers, yes *mothers*, over whose child got credit for a goal in divisions of toddlers that we didn't even keep score or standings—who, unbelievably, spent most of their time just crying on the field or at best running in the wrong direction.

Climbing up the rungs of the insanity ladder brought us promptly to the elected and respected officials from the various soccer clubs, who quite nearly and daily had each other by throats, warmongering over the seconds between field changeups. Of course, this was just spare change compared to the real heavyweights of the *Cuckoo Nest,* the adult teams. Brawling at this level soon became legendary, and sadly was rarely limited to just two men but instead, full rosters of teams having a go at each other so aggressively, that it routinely required an entire squadron of police officers to quell the hostilities.

Out of necessity, we quickly devised and adopted various management strategies in hopes of maintaining some modicum of responsible behaviour in the Madhouse — including buffer time zones between rentals, fines and penalties or suspensions for those unable to contain their thug-like emotional eruptions.

On the upside, we were, for the first time our lives, in the financial black, and as projected, were able that inaugural year to meet our commitments of paying in full for the artificial field, our operational overhead and our lease to the fairgrounds.

The second year, we thankfully managed to discharge, in full, our combined student and consolidation loans and gratefully repay Diane's parents, with interest, for their help in getting us going.

And the third year, as we expanded the operation to include outdoor soccer registration, we decided to spend a little on ourselves—and boy oh boy, did we ever go to town!

Fancy's Fool

Being blessed with the opportunity to do things that we would never have otherwise been able to do, we sat down as a family and brainstormed a kind of bucket, slash wish list, that kicked off by taking the kids to do some serious globetrotting!

Naturally, The Magic Kingdom in Orlando was our first stop, followed then by two circumnavigations of the Florida Panhandle. From there we went on to basking beneath palms on the white sand beaches of the Caribbean, skiing the slopes of Blackcomb in Whistler British Columbia, surfing the waves in Oahu and even attending the World Cup of Soccer in Munich, Germany.

Alongside this scrapbook of incredible travel experiences, we were able to finally vacate our decrepit shed and build a real home on a small acreage of rolling land that we hoped would allow Talon his dream of having a dirt bike and the girls to have, what every girl wants to have, a pony.

And that my friends, was our big mistake in waiting!

· · ·

RIDING HIGH on the laurels of our success, and believing that we could do no wrong, we naively committed ourselves to the near fatal fiscal error of becoming involved with horses— which all began quite innocently with the seemingly harmless purchase of two rather inexpensive yearlings, of no particular breed, from a local farmer, that one might have affectionately referred to as *just a couple of equine mutts.*

Having myself as a child lived and laboured weekends on my father's hobby farm, I had learned something not only about horses but about building fences and paddocks, bailing hay and in general caring for livestock as well. Moreover, my father's life long and singular passion was breeding thoroughbreds—in hopes of going down in the annals of history as having produced a contender for the Derby. Unfortunately, for my little sister and I, this frequently meant arduously long Saturdays at the track, passing the time by collecting and organizing multi-coloured wagering tickets discarded about the grandstand floor.

My mother, no less the aficionado for the racing industry, commissioned herself, post-divorce, to working seven days a week in the backstretch—grooming and eventually training an unsuccessful collection of raggle-taggle glue sticks that had me as a young teenager, reluctantly hot walking and mucking out stalls in the ungodly dark hours of the morning.

Needless to say, by the time I had left the nest at sixteen I fully expected that whatever it was that became of me would certainly have nothing to do with horses!

But what would life be if it didn't toss the occasional curveball at you?

It follows then, that despite what reservations or childhood misgivings I might have held about horses, the incessant "please daddy" *pleas* of my daughters for ponies of their own, eventually, "ahem," broke me down.

Our idea was to start with young untrained fillies, that would allow the girls to develop an understanding and appreciation for the duties, responsibilities, and care of the animals before being able to ride them. When Diane and I felt the time was right, we would have their horses trained and the girls could begin lessons that might lead to family outings at weekend shows and hopefully a line of ribbons hanging in the barn.

In the months preceding the arrival of ponies we spent an enjoyable time together as a family renovating the old outbuilding on our property, adding stalls, and building fences for paddocks. I remember the excitement in the air was no less than palpable as the van slowly backed down the laneway to finally deliver to us Rags and Spice. Rags for Heidi because she had wrapped around her foreleg a ragged towel to protect a small cut, and Spice for Karly, because like Karly, she arrived to us with an ostentatious personality.

Unexpectedly, I soon found, as did Diane, that working with the girls' horses was not only an enjoyable experience but that the daily routine of cleaning and brushing had an almost therapeutic effect on us. So much so that we frequently would let the children sleep in— heading out ourselves instead to work in the peace and tranquility of the barn.

The invigorating aroma of freshly broken hay, the radio quietly playing in the background and the boisterous chirping of the sparrows on the rafters is a place and experience that must be said can genuinely leave its mark on your soul.

By the first heavy snowfall of that year Rags and Spice had nearly doubled in size, as we all were working together training them to walk smartly on a shank and trot attentively on a lead line. In fact, so confident were we in our training methods and results, that one morning while the kids were at school, Diane and I stupidly decided to walk the horses down the road to customize further and calm their senses.

Well, we hadn't gotten ten feet onto the street when a car suddenly came barreling around the corner that so spooked and startled Spice that she uncontrollably began rearing up on her hind legs and backing her way in a panic across the road and into the snow-laden ditch. My poor Diane, having had a life and death grip on the shank was instantly catapulted from the ground and went sailing through the air like superman, crashing and careening spread eagle and face down into the snow.

Unable to offer physical assistance, as from across the road I was myself trying to manage and calm Rags, I pleaded out loud, "Hun, let her go, we will catch her after!"

But still firmly mug-implanted in the depths of the bank, she only raised her head and while angrily spitting out bits of ice cried back, "No, I'm not letting go! She'll get hit by a car!"

BY NOW SEVERAL vehicles had lined up behind one another and had begun slowly rubbernecking their way past my dear spouse—spectating in horror at this poor woman who was now being cruelly drawn and quartered through an icy gutter—plowing face first through heaps and piles of freshly fallen powder!

Struggling to breathe underneath the avalanche mounding and stockpiling up over her head, she quick thinkingly flipped over onto her back— while remarkably maintaining an iron lock grip on the shank.

Poor Spice, still opting for flight over fight, began dragging poor screaming Diane like a ski sledge down the side of the roadway—a ski sledge without boots that is— still perfectly seeded and extruding from the snow precisely where my dear wife had just recently vacated them.

You know, I couldn't say with any degree of absolute certainty, but eyeballing it, I'd have hedged a guess that the distance between the large swale of snowy embankment down the way and the Polar Express now steaming *full speed ahead* towards it, couldn't have been more than, well, a furlong.

"Diane! Just let go of the damn rope!"

But it was too late, for at that very moment Spice sprang like a showjumper, clearing the embankment, and in so doing, sent my beloved sling-shotting up the swale and into the air like a *freestyle Olympian*—returning to the earth with a wind-knocking thud that thankfully at least jarred loose her grip on the shank. As Spice tore predictably off and out of sight, I was ultimately able to intervene by managing Rags in one hand, while with the other, helping a mistreated missus gently back onto her feet—and eventually back to her boots.

"Look, we'll just take Rags back to the barn and then go and find Spice, it will be fine, stop worrying"— trying my best to console her fears, while congratulating her heroic and valiant efforts. Gratefully, no rescue mission was ever required or undertaken, because once we'd returned to the barn, we found that Spice had long since doubled back and was standing in the open doorway of her stall, happily munching away on a freshly fluffed flake of alfalfa.

With little more than a bruised ego and the experience tucked away for safekeeping, not to mention a good laugh to boot, we pressed on with our horsey lives entirely unaware that the gods above had not as yet been sufficiently entertained and were now preparing themselves to call for an encore.

This arrived the following week by post, inconspicuously disguised as a harmless catalogue, indexing the offerings for the upcoming Mixed Winter CTHS Thoroughbred Auction at Toronto's prestigious Woodbine Racetrack. Confused as to how we'd even come to be put on the mailout list for the event—*although I suspected divine intervention*— my first instinct, given my childhood *begrudgments*, was to fire this sucker straight into the trash!

However, given our recent experiences with Rags and Spice and the enjoyment we took in their care, I began to see my parent's passions for the *Sport of Kings* in a new light. As a result of which, I soon found myself ruffling through the pages of hip numbers and pedigrees. With Diane too, taking an interest, it wasn't long before we found ourselves becoming a little intoxicated with the whole affair, spending considerable time educating ourselves to the particular lineages that had produced so many famous champions— like the immortal Secretariat and the undisputed king of all thoroughbred studs, the great Canadian, Northern Dancer!

The catalogue of mares, foals and yearlings also managed to capture the interest of our girls—especially Heidi, who, even at twelve, and the scholar of the family, spent several evenings highlighting the names and the pages of the hips she believed had the best chance of becoming the next Triple Crown winner.

Now armed with a new enthusiasm for the thoroughbred industry, but of course having no intention of actually buying, we enthusiastically made plans to attend the auction and see firsthand and for ourselves what this whole thing was all about.

The night of the sale was uncommonly warm for that November and was cast beneath a brilliant canopy of starlight. The auction pavilion was located at the rear of Woodbine's backstretch, guarding row upon row of barns and stalls open to the public for the viewing and the consideration of prospective offerings for the evening's event. Diane and I, pretending to be wealthy buyers, began touring the shedrows, locating the torn page corners in our catalogue, and like the groups of other well-dressed horsemen, requesting the grooms to bring out and show us our favourites.

Inside, the auditorium was stacked to the rafters with tiered seating, all looking down upon a small stage, roped off and elegantly posted with horse head statuettes and beautiful bouquets of red and white poinsettias. Center stage, a towering pedestal stood impressively beneath a large viewing screen, providing the evening's auctioneer with a grand pulpit from which he could preside over the crowd of excited patrons. Adjacent to the auction auditorium was a large hall, floored with earth, showcasing the first dozen or so mares waiting for their numbers to be announced. Between all of this was the concession area, where behind a long counter, several bartenders donning black tie and vests, were feverishly shaking cocktails and pouring champagne for a line of customers eager to get to into their seats before the call of Hip #1.

Reveling in all the excitement, Diane and I, like pilots unknowingly suffering from altitude hypoxia, were unwittingly becoming infected with horse fever—a dangerous condition made worse by the rapid consumption of more than just a few whiskey sours!

But the atmosphere was electric, as the handlers began bringing in beautiful thoroughbreds one after another. Without taking a breath, the auctioneer began calling out bids, tempting others to bid higher by interjecting the accomplishments of the particular pedigrees. The spotters, carefully spaced around the auditorium, would suddenly and passionately throw up their hands when they maneuvered another buyer to chime in, prompting the auctioneer to become even louder and more boisterous in his rant.

Encapsulated and riveted by all the action, we now watched as the yearlings began entering the ring.

"Look, Hun," Diane excitedly exclaimed while turning to the page of the filly that had just been brought onto the stage. "This one is Heidi's favourite! —see here, she circled the foal's mother because her name was, *Appealing Heidi*."

I'm not really sure what happened after that. The last thing I remember was making eye contact with the spotter, having some mystical premonition, and then tossing my hand up into the air.

"Martin! Oh my god!" looking as if she'd seen a ghost. "What the hell are you doing?"

"I don't know?" I poured back, "I think it's the whiskey sours!"

And before we even had a chance to say one more word to each other, over the loudspeaker, the auctioneer's voice came bellowing out, "$5,000 going once, $5,000 going twice," a long pause...

"Oh no!"

Slamming his gavel down, "*Sold!* " to the idiot in the tenth row who has no idea what he's doing!"

Instantaneously it was like I was storming the beach in Saving Private Ryan. Everything was a haze and I didn't even know where I was or what just happened. Like a zombie I just sat and stared at the runner, leaping joyously up the steps to our seat to congratulate me and get my signature on the sales slip.

"I don't believe it Martin! Now what are we supposed to do? And how are we going to get her home? I don't think she's going to fit in the car!"

"Well you started it with the this is Heidi's favourite crap!"

"I never dreamed you were going to put your hand up — and by the way you're just supposed to nod you know, not shoot your arm right up and out of its socket!"

"Insults, ya, that's going help!" And for a while at least, the arguing continued until we had accepted the fact and settled into the understanding that whatever the cause and effect, we now owned a racehorse!

Once we had managed to adjust our attitudes properly, we excused ourselves from the auction hall, in order to lick our wounds, regroup and now decide how to handle the situation.

The first order of business was to locate one of the on-site transport companies listed in the catalogue and make arrangements for delivery. After we'd managed that, we then proceeded directly back to the barn for a *meet and greet* with the breeder, and of course, our bag of bones, who was going to be, so I tried to consoled myself, our ticket to sipping mint juleps in the clubhouse at the *Run for the Roses.*

At the shedrow we were met by a pretty young stable hand, lugging back from the taps, two brimming horse buckets full of water and asking if we were here to see *Hip #134.*

"Yes," I replied, still thinking to myself, *I can't believe this is happening!*

Following a cheerful, "this way please," she guided us to a stall at the end of the through-way, adorned with a large laminated copy of the catalogue page for our filly. Promptly plunking down her buckets, she quickly twisted up her long hair into a bun, securing it with a pencil retrieved from the pocket of her dungarees—in order, I supposed, to politely introduce herself with some semblance of presentability.

"Hi, I'm Jen," shaking our hands, "and this is your new dark bay filly."

"Wow, she is beautiful!" Diane remarked. I had to admit she was indeed that. Tall, stylish and more midnight black than dark bay. She had a regal tuff of forelock banged just above brilliant eyes and a magnificently manicured stretch of mane that trickled elegantly along her neckline.

Leaning on my experience, I asked, "She seems quite large and muscular for a yearling though don't you think?"

"Huh-huh, well, she's a January baby, and because her mother refused to nurse, we had to bottle feed her." Then she giggled a little, and while giving our filly the once over, noted, "guess we kinda overdid it eh? Do you know what you're going to call her?"

"Know what we are going to call her?" I laughed, "We don't even know where we are going to put her!"

Snickering back, "Well, we call her Daisy."

"Daisy?" I highbrowed back to her with a sarcastic little smirk.

"Huh- huh, it's her barn name, you know, like a nickname."

Daisy, I thought to myself, that rhymes nicely with crazy, just like this whole evening has been! *Perfect—crazy Daisy!*

Hardly could I have known that that little term of endearment would shortly become an intricately woven part of our daily vocabulary.

Crazy Daisy

The following morning we hurriedly created new accommodations for Daisy in the barn directly across from that of Rags and Spice, then returned to the house to anxiously await the arrival of the transport van. We even granted the children—who were openly of the opinion that their parents should be committed—rare permission to play hooky from school.

By late afternoon, long past the expected delivery time, we were becoming increasingly concerned that something was wrong. Fair to say we all were more than relieved to finally see the truck and trailer now slowly reversing its way down the laneway.

"Sorry for the delay, folks!" exclaimed the rather grey, worn and torn, unquestionably track-hardened driver as he jumped down from the cab to the ground.

"Had a lot of difficulties loading her, refused to go on, pretty spirited that one is."

Inside the trailer, Daisy was living up to her chauffeur's assertions by snorting, calling out loudly and kicking angrily at the ramp door.

"Oh boy!" I started nervously thinking to myself, handling a couple of low-key burros like Rags and Spice was one thing, but managing a sizeable high-strung thoroughbred, I knew well enough was entirely something else.

As Diane rounded up and herded the children away from the trailer, the driver/handler, now at Daisy's head and I at midship, began slowly backing her out and down off the ramp. As she began to emerge from the hold, we all were taken aback at the sheer size of her that was, in comparison to our own two horses, nothing less than titanic. Relieved that all four hooves were finally and firmly afoot on terra-firma, I was then handed, with noticeable relief, the keys, bid a fond farewell and a final wish of good luck as man and truck, with haste, sped out of sight.

Daisy was, as was I, a sweat-ridden bundle of nerves. Shaking and screaming out at Rags and Spice in the paddock, who pressed tightly against the fence rails, began resonantly calling back causing her, and subsequently me, even more distress and anxiety.

Fearing that she might injure herself tearing and racing about the fields should we turn her out right away, we decided instead to take her immediately to the barn so she could have a moment to securely and safely settle in. Unfortunately, this required and involved having to parade past our own two less than helpful nags, who had now taken to galloping wildly back and forth from end to end of the turnout.

Not yet halfway down the line of fencing, Daisy began

to rear up on her hindquarters, striking out with her forelimbs, like flailing sledgehammers, that if one wasn't extremely careful, could effectively deliver a fatal blow. Instinctively I released the shank with my right hand to give her space, time, and distance to calm, while with my left gripping the knot firmly at the end of the line so as not to lose her completely. Twice more we played out this rodeo show, before Diane and I managed her, dancing and prancing like a dressage champion, to the barn and finally into her stall.

Seemingly even more distraught and agitated, to the point of completely ignoring her grain, she began thrashing about her water pail and kicking the stall walls —angrily ripping out strands of hay from the net and screaming for Rags and Spice out in the paddock.

Resolutely refusing to settle down, we eventually made for the fields to bring in the other two, hoping that their presence in the barn would relieve the innate herd instincts that likely were at least in part of what was causing Daisy so much distress. Thankfully, this finally made some difference, and after some time, she was able to cool her jets enough so as that I felt willing to leave Diane holding vigil at the homestead while I attended to my nightly duties at the soccer Madhouse!

Before sunup the next morning, we were already at work in the barn. Since it was a Saturday, we had enlisted the children's help, including Talon, who, despite his particular disdain for horses, had nonetheless kindly pledged his support for the cause. Along with our little white Shih Tzu, Gertie, who had anything but dislike for horses or anything else with hooves for that matter, the entire family went about mucking out stalls, replenishing food and sweeping up!

Yet despite the harmonious activity in the barn, Daisy was still clearly unsettled and nervously pacing around her stall. More concerningly was that she still had not yet touched her feed.

And as Diane and I were discussing this very issue, my mother, who had gotten wind of what we'd gotten ourselves into, and thanking her lucky stars for giving her an opportunity, even incidentally, to reunite with the racing industry, arrived on the scene.

"I just can't believe you guys bought a horse at the sale! What were you thinking?" she carried on, diminishing our common sensibility as my parents so often liked to do.

"I can assure you we weren't thinking," Diane replied, while casually tossing a familiar unimpressed expression in my general direction.

"Hmmm...she's got good confirmation and a hell of a chest on her, I'll tell you that," continuing to evaluate Daisy's confirmation and at least letting us take some comfort in the thought that perhaps fate had a not dealt us a lemon!

"The problem, mom, is she is not eating!"

After debating the mash mixture ratio and assuring her that we'd been giving her plenty of warm water, she suggested, "She could have injured herself in the van and is in some pain and discomfort." —proceeding to run her hands carefully down Daisy's forelegs looking for swelling or heat. "Nope don't see anything, have you called the breeder as they might know something about this."

Good idea I thought to myself and sent Talon quickly to the house to retrieve the sales catalogue that contained a list of contacts. Hoping to reach Jen, our girl at the sales barn, I was somewhat discouraged when an elderly man with a strong eastern European accent on the other end of the line informed me that, "Jen at barn, but I can helping you?"

So as not to misunderstood, I began to slowly explain who we were, who we'd purchased and the details of our dilemma. In plain English, that she wasn't eating and was still upset and nervous.

"Oh," he came back," I knowing her, that one liking goats, only goats making her feeling good."

Muting the receiver with the palm of my hand, I whispered to mother, "He says she needs a goat."

"That could be," she answered back, hands upon her hips, twisting her lips and nodding," lots of horses on the track have goats in their stalls to keep them company. If she was raised with a goat, that's probably it!"

"Ok," I thanked the gentleman, left him my number, and relayed we'd call back if we had any more problems with Daisy.

Hanging up and firmly putting down the phone, I turned to Diane and with a considerable degree of frustration about my face questioned, "Well, where the hell are we supposed to get a goat?"

"Don't you remember, the man who sold us Rags and Spice had goats, try him."

So, scrolling down my list of contacts, I was soon on the phone with the farmer, who unfortunately conveyed he hadn't any goats that he could sell us but knew of someone only a few miles away that sold goat meat and that maybe he could help.

Pressing on while leaving my mother and her grandchildren in charge of the situation, Diane and I climbed up and into our pickup truck and headed off into the misty sunrise to get *us a goat*!

The house and barns were an easy find, as a large conjoined flag of part Canadian and part Portuguese, was precisely as described, flying proudly at the top of the laneway. A portly and weathered elderly woman wearing a headscarf, parka and skirt, while reeling in a wash line of clothing— strangely in the middle of winter— directed us back to the barns to speak with her husband.

A rugged and ragged, bone-thin, dark-haired man, standing shin-deep in a mudded goat pen, soon began explaining, "My goats for eating, don't know about pet."

Diane, feeling the need to interject, went on to intently re- explain our predicament, whereby he quickly interrupted with a hearty chuckle and pointing, "Ok lady," fanning down his hands at her, "you can have that one, she have red hair just like you."

Still sniggering to himself and placing his cigarette into the hold of his lips to free his hands, he lifted our new red-haired goat into the bed of the truck. To ours, and likely to that of the goat's disbelief, he then proceeded to hogtie her feet together.

"Stop!" cried Diane, "what are you doing?"

"Maybe goat jump out of truck when you driving home." "That's ridiculous, I'll sit in the back with Hillary!"

"Diane, you'll freeze to death!" I tried to argue. "And who the hell is Hillary?"

"Well she needs a name and don't you think she looks like a Hillary?" —professing back in the affirmative while stepping up onto the bumper and hoisting herself into the rear of the truck—promptly then sitting herself down beside and placing her arm around a visibly bewildered billy.

Knowing better than to argue with my wife once she had made up her mind, I instead went about the duty of trading our Portuguese goat herder a fifty-dollar bill in exchange for Hillary and one hogtie rope, now a makeshift leash for Diane's goat.

All the way home I continually checked my rear-view mirror, keeping a careful and watchful eye on the back of Diane and Hillary's heads pressed up against the window with their red hairs fluttering in the wind.

Back at the barn we arrived as if escorting Hollywood royalty on a red-carpet walk. The entire gang, including one insanely over-exuberant Shih Tzu, came pouring out absurdly clambering about trying to get a piece of Hillary.

"Oh my god, she's so cute. Heidi, look at her floppy ears!"

"I like her stumpy horns and black socks."

"Mom, she's got the exact same colour hair as you."

"Kids give her some space! Gertie get out of the way!" I began ordering the lot, attempting to press on with the bigger and more critical issue at hand.

At first, I just held Hillary at the half-open stall door, seeing how Daisy would react. To our relief, this seemed to go very well with nothing more than affectionate sniffing and nuzzling. Feeling confident that we had found the solution to Daisy's ongoing nervousness, I stepped into the stall and put Hillary down onto the floor in front of her.

Well, this didn't go so well! Daisy, acting as if she'd never seen a goat, bug-eyed, backed herself into the corner of the stall, stomping her feet and letting out a piercing loud neigh—as Hillary, to our combined and utter disbelief— fainted!

"Oh no Dad, she had a heart attack!"

"No she didn't, she just fainted, some goats do that."

"I can't believe this"— *muttering to myself*— *"of all the goats in the province of Ontario, what's the chance we get one with a fainting condition?"*

But sure enough, every time Hillary regained consciousness, I'd stand her back up on her feet where she'd take one look at Daisy and immediately topple over again. Up onto her feet, topple back over, up onto her feet, topple back over. Finally, having had enough of this silliness, I turned around to the line of speechless faces pressed up against the outside of the stall bars, proclaiming, with a passed-out Hillary at my feet, "This is ridiculous, we can't leave a fainting goat in here!"

Precisely at that very moment, as if on cue, Hillary, one eye open to the open stall door, rebounded onto her four little hooves and made fast for freedom by scrambling out and down to the end of the barn and bee-lining out into the forest beyond.

The entire group, save me who stayed back to mind the horses, immediately took out after her—clanking and clattering like a mob of medieval villagers— ridiculously parading behind our overly passionate pup hot on the scent of her trail.

Enjoying the moment of comedy, I proceeded to watch as the troop fanned out, much like that of a body search party, still only yards astern of Gertie, exuberantly plowing her flat little face through the snow, with only the tip tops of her ears peering out like pair of periscopes. To Gertie's credit however she quickly and precisely managed to locate poor Hillary, who had fainted while trying to hide behind a large fallen tree trunk.

The motley rescue crew then rapidly formed a tight wagon train circle around Hillary, hoping, no doubt, to prevent a re-escape! From my vantage point at the barn, I could see that the goat posse was now intently conferencing with each other on a plan of recovery. And in hindsight, I might have, and perhaps should have ventured out to help in the retrieval—but in all honestly, I felt fortunate for once not having to be front and center stage of the operation.

Likely believing that neither one of them had the physical strength to singularly hoist and haul a load of goat, they opted instead to transport poor Hillary, pigmy tribe style! Recollective of someone tied by their feet to a stick and on route to an unfortunate encounter with an industrial-sized kettle full of boiling water, my mother clasping her by the back legs and Diane by her front, then began shuffling along back to the barn with Hillary's inverted head flopping and loudly bleating all the way.

The children, sporting bones through their noses, were with zeal lugging along behind and Gertie, proud as a peacock, delightedly bringing up the rear.

Once safely back inside the barn, the kids swiftly wrapped up Hillary in a warm blanket and sat down on a bail of straw, comforting, and nursing her ordeal with warm water, carrots and sweet feed. A wide-eyed, feverishly panting Gertie tucked in alongside, her silly pom-pom tail vigorously vibrating and clearly conveying that she had found new meaning and a new lot in life as a bloodhound.

No sooner had we shut the barn doors and all settled down than did the phone rang.

"Hi, Martin?"

"Yes."

"This is Jen, you called earlier about Daisy?"

"Oh yes, thanks for calling Jen."

She went on to explain apologetically. "I'm sorry, but I forgot to tell you the other night about her special diet. Maybe because she was bottle fed, I'm not exactly sure, but she only likes oats with warm water and apples."

"Did you say *oats*, Jen?"

"Uh-huh."

"*So, oats, not goats!*" I glared at Diane.

On the other end of the line, Jen, while letting out a little snicker, replied rather cheerfully, "Nope, oats not goats."

"Oh for heavens' sake, seriously?"

Well, there was no way in hell that anyone in that barn was going to let me return poor Hillary to the Portuguese meat-market. And so naturally, we spent the remainder of that day building a pen for the new addition to our family —Hillary the Kid!

The misnomer of oats and goats notwithstanding, Daisy's proper porridge of apples and oats was precisely what she was wanting. And once having licked and lapped up her feed tub clean, she quickly and gratefully settled down into a manageable disposition.

So much so, that the very next morning, we'd decided to turn her out into the paddock with Rags and Spice, hoping that after a little expected mare domineering, they'd become good-spirited pasture mates. As it so happened, and much to our delight, after a brief period of tussling, squealing, and shoving, they went happily about the business doing what horses do—eating and shitting!

Once we'd finished up our chores in the barn, the five of us retired to the house to wash up and eagerly await the arrival of Diane's Sunday morning breakfast of French toast with maple syrup and bacon!

Amidst the eventual and predictable argument over who had rights to the last strip of peameal, there came quite unexpectedly a loud knock at the front door.

"Who could that be on a Sunday morning?" Diane wholly puzzled called out.

Sliding my chair back from the table and relaying, "I'll get it," I quickly opened the door only to see a well-dressed middle-aged woman made up if she were on her way visiting or perhaps to church.

"Excuse me," She began rather nervously to question. "But do you own a black horse?"

Pausing for a moment, and glancing past her shoulder to the paddock to only see Rags and Spice, I cautiously answered back, "Yes—why?"

"Well, it's on the road, and I think it's injured!"

LIKE A FIREHOUSE DRILL, the five of us scrambled to get our boots and coats on before racing up the driveway, shocked to find, that in fact, Daisy was standing outside the fencing at the roadside, knee-deep in a bank of blood-stained snow!

"Oh my God Martin, she's killed herself!" Diane screamed out loud as we rushed to her side.

It didn't require much surmising to see what had happened. For whatever reason, Daisy had tried to jump the fence line and in the process of doing so, had scraped the skin off her shins down to the very bone. Worse yet, she had managed in the process, to gore herself on a splintered tree stump, leaving a fist-sized gaping hole in her chest cavity— the displaced flesh dangling horrifically down between her front legs.

Quickly I sent the children to fetch buckets of warm water and as many towels as they could find, while I held and tried to console Daisy, shaking and quite obviously in shock.

Diane, having brought her phone, immediately called

the emergency veterinary hotline. Yet despite our dyer circumstance, the call center apologetically relayed that because it was the weekend it could take up to an hour for the veterinarian to arrive on the scene.

Minutes later the children returned in a winded panic with water and a box full of towels and tape. Fearing that trying to move her might cause more injury, we did our best to stop the bleeding by cleaning and wrapping homestyle bandaging about her legs— and reinserting and holding in place her chest flesh as best that we could at the roadside.

Given the considerable loss of blood, I began worrying that Daisy might at any point soon drop to the ground, so had the children who'd been heroically holding the towels to her injuries move back to a safe distance. Finally, after what seemed like days, the vet eventually arrived— and like a combat field medic, immediately began to treat Daisy's wounds right there in the ditch.

After administering a gob of sedation and a generous helping of freezing, he meticulously and painstakingly began stitching her breast back together. Sewing along, he rather calmly, given the circumstances, informed us that, "If you're a horse and you're going to get injured, the auxiliary area is probably the better place to do it. Those cuts on her legs look skin deep, so I don't suspect any fractures—she should be fine."

You've got to be kidding me, I thought to myself— because from where I sat, this poor unfortunate nag had at very least one foot firmly planted in the grave.

"Nope, seen worse! But we will need to send her to the

equine hospital in Hillsburgh to make sure she recovers without complications."

Two thoughts now came to mind, how long and how much?

Nevertheless, remembering that which does not kill us only makes us stronger, we eased a bruised and battered Daisy back to her stall to await the arrival of the horse ambulance.

OVER THE NEXT SIX WEEKS, we kept in regular touch with the staff at the equine hospital and made every effort to visit Mrs. Money Pit whenever we had the chance—never forgetting to pack an oven-load of homemade oatmeal cinnamon cookies, which Daisy loved to devour by the boxfuls.

After a progressive, steady, and uncomplicated recovery, Daisy was finally returned to our farm on the first of March, apparently unscathed and none the worse for the experience.

Indeed, we soon observed a noticeable and distinctive difference in her behaviour and attitude. She seemed more mature and more relaxed around the lot of us, including even Hillary. It was almost as if coming face to face with her mortality had given her a new appreciation for life. And perhaps, as well, a new appreciation for the loving and caring family that had nearly killed her in the first place!

In the weeks that followed Daisy's posture continued to strengthen with an abundance of physical and emotional confidence. Impressed with her growing stature, and in possession of a clean bill of health, not to mention repeated approvals from her doctor, we decided to start her on basic training. A friend and neighbour, having horses of her own, recommended to us a young girl living nearby, that was well known in the local equine community for her expertise in training show horses and breeding warmbloods.

Andrea was in every sense of the word the image of an Equestrian. Tallish, thin, ruggedly attractive, and discerningly attired with the accoutrements of her trade. Unfettered by the frivolous frills of fashion and style, hers' was a world of passionate practicality—easily recognized by steel toes and chaps upon denim, ponytail under cap, fleece behind leather and of course, a crop tucked faithfully away in the backside of her britches.

Diane and I would enjoy nothing more than to sit and sip hot tea on the porch of our house while watching Andrea out in the sand ring working her magic with Daisy. Like a violinist's bow teasing the strings into singing a heavenly melody, so it was with Andrea and her incredible way with horses.

Having mastered the groundwork, she was soon able to mount and impressively maneuver Daisy about the ring merely with the slightest pressures of her legs. In the short time that followed, they could be regularly seen trotting and cantering around the ring, moving together in complete unison, in every way a moving picture of artistry in motion.

As her training progressed, Andrea would frequently

take time to remind us that Daisy, unlike her warmbloods, was bred for speed, rather than jumping over oxers. And although many are indeed retired to the world of showjumpers, thoroughbreds, with their thin legs, raised constitution and high temperament, were in the first place designed for performance in racing.

Giving this notion much careful deliberation, and after consulting with our veterinarian, we began to consider the possibility of allowing Daisy to dust off some of her hereditary ambitions at the track. My mother, who frequently had her oar in when it came to Daisy's interests, insisted that "one horse trackside training was an owner-operator affair. Ridiculous to spend money on trainers when I still have a license and we could certainly do this ourselves!"

So often did she continually prattle on about her point of view that eventually Diane and I conceded and granted her permission to make applications for stall space at Woodbine's backstretch.

Despite a lengthy waiting list, mother managed by the first of June to arm-wrestle us a couple of stalls, one for feed and one for, well, Daisy. But before we could take up official residence at the track, there was the matter of three essential administrative duties and formalities that were, for Diane and me, a lot of fun to address.

First on the list was selecting and registering a stable name for us to race under. For this, I suggested naming our stable after my grandmother, as a testimonial to her kind demeanour that I believed helped shape the better half of my personality. And so, Anna Hein was condensed, reformed, and proudly relabeled as *Annahein Racing Stables*.

The second to-do was to design, record and order the colours and patterns of our jockey silks. Unselfishly, Diane insisted that the colours should in some way, be a representation of the person for whom we'd named the stable after. Given my grandmother's German Heritage, we agreed on three simple bars of black, red, and gold that would nobly do the trick.

Finally, and no less importantly, it was the matter of giving Daisy her racing name—not an uncomplicated issue as Diane, the kids and I went through several drafts and re-drafts before eventually resorting to having to pick her name out of a hatful of our favourites. Fortune, favouring the foolish, it was my name that was pulled and shortly after that, officially registered, becoming attached formally to Daisy forever, *Creosote*.

Diane would always say about Daisy's new title, "ah I could love it or leave it"—and be that as it may, it was actually Daisy's rich coat of tar-black that always reminded me of the fence stain my father used on his farm and the strange name that seemed to always resonate in my memory - *Creosote*.

The Pocket Universe

I t was an absolutely picture perfect morning in mid-June that Daisy stepped up calmly and confidently onto the ramp and into the transport van—now bound for her new home within the hollows of the grand theatre of Canadian racing that is Woodbine Racetrack.

Surrounded by a sprawling, ever-changing and ever-modernizing urban jungle, the backstretch at Woodbine is a defiantly unaltered place that time has utterly forgotten —a world entirely unto its own. From the very moment you pass through the *East Gate,* you become delightfully enchanted by the sounds, scents, and imagery of a simpler and more sensible era.

Quietly rising up from behind row upon row of barns, the morning sun begins to gently illuminate the sanded pathways leading to and from the tunnel at the main track —already dappled with the shadows of regal thoroughbreds and dutiful lead-ponies, sauntering along, two or three abreast, their exercise riders high atop chittering and chattering on about nothing.

At the barns, the endless procession of shedrows are

bustling and teeming with life—as riotous brown sparrows noisily arguing over little bits of grain are desperately trying to avoid the hooves and the boots of the hot walkers—and the pawing prides of tattered cats, scratching out their living, but sadly missing a bit of ear or a snip of this or that.

An international and eclectic community of curiously outdated characters, both old and young, are busy filling and hauling hot buckets of steaming water and half barrels of steaming manure, that drift out plumes of that pleasant earthy aroma that seems to just fill the place.

In the courtyards between, a handful of jockeys and trainers are queued up at the coffee truck, intently debating the condition book—oblivious to the feed man in his dependable plaid shirt, who, with a pencil tucked behind his ear is diligently itemizing bags of oats, bales of hay and the fluorescent green strips of sod that horses are so fond of.

At the epicenter of this miniature island universe stands unchanged, a timeless relic, affectionately referred to by its dedicated patronage plainly and simply as *the Kitchen*. A hubbub of hooting and hollering, bickering and bantering, it is a place where unshaven old men, donning white undershirts and dirtied aprons, labour behind over-lipsticked cashiers in curlers and kerchiefs, who still serve up mixed greens, mashed potatoes and gravied beef for breakfast.

And it was precisely here, in this pocket island paradise, that our little convoy arrived that morning to deliver our champion, our hand in the game and our entry in the race to barn 14A.

Our plan was simple, to the point and went a little like this:

I'd set my alarm for 4:20 am every day, slide out of bed, grumble my way to the loo, then wash my teeth and brush my face, wrestle into my track- gear, kiss goodbye a still snoozing Diane and make the hour drive down to Woodbine. My mother, living closer by, and having long since given Daisy her breakfast, would be anxiously waiting for my arrival— as per her expectations, not one minute later than 5:30 am.

After several good mornings to the clan at the end of 14A, and of course to Daisy, I'd proceed to brush body, mane and tail while Mother picked the crap out of Daisy's feet.

Looking to make sure no one was coming, Daisy and I would then quickly exit the stall, and like a link in a chain, join the parade of others, either warming up or cooling down around the shedrow. As I was shouting out "coming through" or "heads up" while making half-circle turns at the mid-point intersection of the barns, mom would be sprinting to the kitchen to get us some java, an order of brown toast for her and a package of those delicious donuts with the chocolate icing and whipped cream inside for me.

With Daisy now back in her stall, we would take a moment to chat and have little breakfast while waiting for the exercise rider, who to my mother's regular frustration, would be for one excuse or another dependably late.

Eventually, once we saw that the rider was coming, we'd rush to get Daisy tacked up just in time to hoist the little guy or gal into the saddle directly. Then, while simultaneously relaying the instructions for the morning's program, we'd send them off on and on their way to either the sand ring, training track or eventually and hopefully to the main track to record some good workout times.

While horse and rider were off doing their business, mother would fetch soapy pails of hot water for Daisy's post-workout bath, while I mucked out her stall and swept up.

Upon her return from exercising, a warm bath and a 45-minute cool out around the shedrow, I would by 10:30 am tip my hat, wave goodbye and make my way up to the Madhouse to clean up the carnage left over from games of soccer the night before.

Cursing the slobs that the men from the late-night men's league were—I'd begin my duties by circling the field picking up and bagging callously discarded water and sport-drink bottles, forgotten clothing, beer cans, tape and candy wrappers. Worse still was having to dig out, on my hands and knees, imbedded chewing gum from the fibres of the turf. A god awful duty that was at least one step above the degradation of having to clean the men's washroom— whereupon I'd have regularly called them dirty little pigs, but that would have been an unfair insult to, well, dirty little pigs!

Post clean up, I'd head for home, stopping at the little deli in Caledon to pick up a sandwich for myself and my dear Diane—who, by the time I walked through the front door, had already gotten the kids off to school, cleaned the entire house and barn and was busy at the computer soccering her life away.

By 2:00 pm, I was ready and looking forward to a little schnoozel on the couch while Diane toddled off to town to get something for dinner.

At 4:00 pm, the kids would arrive home from school, have some snacks and head out to bring Rags and Spice into the barn—returning to the house just in time to wash up, have a sit-down family dinner and then hug me as I headed back down to manage the nightly mob of maniacs at the Madhouse!

A hectic, albeit exhaustive plan and schedule that we soon discovered only had one little flaw, one little hiccup and one small tiny little glitch—that being of course that Daisy hated the track! Conveying to us, in not so many words that, but without a shedrow of doubt..., "there is no way in hell that I'm participating in this ridiculously stupid idea of yours!"

This rebellious attitude of hers hardly required any time to manifest and fester itself properly, but rather emerged right out of the starting gate. One morning after having sent Daisy and her exercise rider out to the sand ring to do a little light trotting, mother and I were bewildered to see her suddenly returning only minutes later, ambling down the shedrow fully under tack but not under the rider.

"Daisy, what are you doing here?" I began to interrogate her while holding the reigns and scanning behind, absurdly hoping the jockey might be playing a practical joke by hiding under her tail.

Returning with a pail of water in each hand, my mother was no less shocked and began shouting, "Where the hell is the rider?"

It wasn't too long after that, that the exercise boy, in an angry fluster, arrived at the barn furiously fretting, "Your horse is nuts and nearly killed me out there!"—going on to explain how with malicious intent, Daisy had at the ring, thrown him into the railings before trying to finish the job by stomping him to death!

Given that word travels around the backstretch faster than Secretariat's 2:24 minute record at the Belmont, by the following day we were having an impossible time trying to find an exercise rider. Mother, utilizing her powers of persuasion, and calling in just about every favour she had, eventually hooked and bridled a hungry for dollars apprentice to give it another go!

This time around, believing and praying that yesterday's fiasco had something to do with the sand ring, we saddled Daisy up and sent her out to the training track. But not ten minutes later she unbelievably returned to the barn just as she had the day before—rider less! The poor kid having gone immediately to seek some minor medical treatment for a sprained wrist, later recounted to us that, Daisy had as if possessed, charged uncontrollably down the track, and while veering off at the turn, scaled the railings and then viciously dismounted him into the bushes before fleeing back to the barn.

. . .

WELL, not long after that incident, the track Stewards, who had gotten word of what was going on and concerned that our *dog and pony show* was going to get someone killed, soon issued to us a stern ultimatum, *shape up or ship* out!

At this point even my mother had to admit that this wasn't going very well, and by the next day, unable to enlist even the most eager of riders, we finally made the hard decision to pack it in.

Of course, just as we were preparing to do so, fate intervened, as Rob-49 and his wife turned up unannounced at the barn to see if they could offer us some assistance!

As he began, rather slowly and somewhat off the mark to introduce themselves to us as a freelance groom and exercise rider, I couldn't help but notice that life had run these two poor souls through the wringer more than once.

Outwardly and clearly beyond their years, each owning thinly greyed and tattered hair, withered features, weathered skin and misplaced or unaccounted for sets of bridgework— they nevertheless professed to own a unique and special way with horses both on the tack and at the equestrian center they worked at in the afternoons.

Skeptical as I was, having been through the wringer myself more than once, but knowing better than to ever judge a book by its cover, I fatefully proceeded to introduce them to our beloved problem child!

Faster than you could say "holy horse whisperer," Daisy's demeanor miraculously transformed before our very eyes. Moving and interacting about the stall together, it was as if all three had been previously and tenderly acquainted in some past-life incarnation.

"That's amazing!" I whispered out, believing I was thinking to myself, but then startled as Cindy, with a confident smile that seemed to remove the years from her expression, explained, that "horses are very intuitive and sensitive creatures— unfortunately, most of these folks down here are just too dam intense for these gentle souls."

In that instant, I experienced a personal transformation of my own, becoming a believer in claims of human to animal telepathic communication. And I can say without reservation that the buzz in the air at that very moment in time was no less than palpable!

Certainly not being one to look a gift horse in the mouth, so to speak, we were now with our newly found horse whisperers on board, once again, back in the game.

Rob-49

R ob-49, because as we soon discovered, should we need to leave a message for him at the rooming house where he boarded, the floor manager, to do so, required a first name and a bed number —Rob-49!

At any rate, he and his wife Cindy, *the 49-ers*, regardless of rank or file were shortly making impressive strides forward with Daisy's delicate temperament and training! Myself, and eventually my mother, soon became more or less relegated, quite thankfully I might add, to the position of hired hands and to the duties of feed and clean—while Rob focused all his efforts on the proper grooming and tacking of Daisy, making all perfectly ready for her daily exercise beneath the steady and seasoned hands of his Cindy.

It was indeed a pleasure to watch the three of them in action. Every morning once Rob had finished brushing and picking Daisy's feet, she would, as if going into a trance, begin to stretch her muscles like a professional human athlete warming up. She achieved this self-taught feat by extending her forelimbs out to the stall walls, arching her back in a downward dog position until the girth of her belly nearly touched the straw bedding of the floor. Then, as soon as bridle and saddle were inspected and firmly in place, 49A would give a leg up to 49B, pat Daisy on the ass and confidently smile as she and she went nattering together down the shedrow and out of sight.

It wasn't long before Daisy had graduated her way up from the sand ring to the training track, soon earning her gate pass by demonstrating that she could enter, stand quietly and depart the starting gate without quarrel or measurable amount of brouhaha! Having earned her wings, by mid-July, Daisy had advanced, ready, willing and able to take on the big leagues out at the main track.

With the children out of school for summer holidays and responsibly assuming the responsibilities of self-breakfasting and barning, Diane was regularly free to join our crew at the track— and more often than not, we'd leave my mother to sweep up the shedrow while trotting off and excitedly ambling up the grassy bank to the backside railing of the main track to watch Daisy in action.

At first Cindy would take her on a gentle two-mile gallop twice around the oval. Watching intently from the railings, Diane and I would have the pleasure of eavesdropping in on the discourse as they squabbled past us.

"Easy sweetheart, easy," whilst hunched up off the saddle, firmly in the stirrups and with a tight grip on the reigns. "Steady now, steady girl."—Daisy's neck and head curled over, hugging the inside rail, snorting and breathing in perfect time with the thud of her hooves hitting the sand.

Upon returning to the barn and after each subsequent outing to the track, Rob and my mother would painstakingly go over every square inch of Daisy's legs and feet to make entirely sure she hadn't become injured, sore or worst of all, bucked her shins—a common painful condition of two year old thoroughbreds in training as a result of overstressing their fragile and thin bones.

Confident that she was mentally and physically sound, Cindy moved Daisy into the next phase of her training —breezing!

It was nothing less than exhilarating to watch as Cindy eased her along the straightaway of the backstretch, warming her up before hitting the quarter pole and then giving Daisy some throttle—accelerating into the turn at a pace that even from our distant vantage point was breathtaking.

With the uncomfortably hot and humid days of July now far behind us, we suddenly found ourselves coming into the quiet last weeks of August and telltale buzz of the cicada bugs reminding us that fall was now just around the corner. And just as our children began excitedly preparing themselves for another school year, we began eagerly preparing Daisy to clock her first official workout.

It was a significant hurdle for us and our prodigy to cross over as it meant picking not only a jockey but also a new set of hands at the wheel. After several team conferences on the matter and a strong recommendation from Cindy, the duty and honour of guiding Daisy to the

Winner's Circle fell upon the steady shoulders of Lori Davis.

Firmly believing in our collective opinion that a female hand was likely an essential part of the equation when it came to successfully *driving Miss Daisy* around the track, Lori was a natural choice, as not only did she have a similar physical and personal disposition to that of Cindy, but an impressive winning streak to boot.

The day before her workout Lori took the time and came by the barn to meet her mount.

"So, this is her eh? Big girl, nice confirmation!"

Standing with her arms crossed and smartly decked to the nines in quintessential jockey gear that included a goggled helmet, vested body armour and a crop jetting out of her knee-high black boots, she continued on to compliment Daisy for a while longer— inadvertently making us all feel that perhaps a day at the races was now in the turn for home.

The following morning as Daisy, calmly under Lori's steady hand, entered the tunnel and out onto the main track, mother and trainer called up to the clockers high in their tower, "Creosote—two furlongs."

Like giddy little schoolchildren, the five of us giggled and clambered our way up to the side the railing, hoping for a safely earned black-type workout.

Our gang of silly onlookers soon became nervously silent as Daisy and Lori finally came past us gradually picking up speed until they hit the quarter pole and then put the pedal to the metal.

"Wow!" Diane cried out, at the burst of sudden speed

and ease of movement between horse and rider as if they were but one.

Gracefully striding tightly against the inside rail, the instant Daisy's whiskers finally contacted the furlong marker, Rob hammered down on his stopwatch, pursed his lips, gave a quick firm nod and pronounced,

"Twenty-five flat, not bad, not bad at all!"

As the last lazy days of August had slipped away leaving us reveling in cool September mornings and admiring the magnificent hues of red and gold leaves painting away the brilliant blue skies of early fall— Daisy, having accumulated by then several more promising and longer workouts, was now prepared herself, by the first of October for a chance to break her maiden!

Believing ourselves that she might indeed be ready, and still in possession of a clean bill of health from the track vet, we headed off to the racing office on the morning of the seventh of October to enter Daisy onto the card for the following Saturday.

A century-old tradition of owners and trainers had gathered around the strangely elongated shaped bingo ball puller waiting with great anticipation for the call out of the post positions for the daily entries. After what seemed like hours, it was finally time to decide the allocations for the 20k claimers.

"Creosote—Post 5," the secretary called out.

Mother standing behind Rob and me, slapped our backs positively announcing,

"Nearly the middle of a twelve-horse field, in a five-furlong sprinter, just where we want to be boys!"

A Day at the Races

Nothing to that point in our lives had offered up quite the same flavours of excitement as getting ready for not only our day at the races, but hopefully a picture in the Winner's Circle— and god willing, a heap of prize money dumped back into the depleted coffers of Annahein Stables!

I had to admit that even the ritzy women with their elaborate hats, chic dresses, and fashionable heels at Churchill Downs on Derby Day, couldn't have shined any brighter than the girls and Diane did on Daisy Day.

Palazzo pants, camisoles, bolero jackets, fascinators, pocket purses and pumps were the statements for the event and made for a picture-perfect picture of wholesome regality. Not to be entirely outdone, Talon and I, in shined up snappy loafers, black suits, white shirts and red paisley ties, like gentlemen held open the doors for the ladies as we entered the prestigiously elegant Woodbine Club— to await the bugler's famous *Call to the Post* at the start of race number three.

Mother herself, quite fancifully attired, sporting

however the most ridiculously oversized organza derby hat, was by the time we had arrived, already loading up a plateful of culinary delights from the buffet table that was fit and dressed for English royalty—chilled lobster, prosciutto-wrapped asparagus, herbed prime rib with merlot au jus and a mile-long charcuterie bouquet of fine Italian meats and French cheeses—all flaming out at the end of the line in a massive china terrine filled with cherries jubilee!

The view from our table alongside the towering walls of glass high above and overlooking the tiers of outdoor patios and grandstand seating was spectacular. No less breathtaking was the enormity of the racecourse itself.

Two-mile-long ovals, the inner, an artificial all-weather track, and the outer a plush green band of turf encircled the magnificently manicured infield of beautiful ponds, fountains, trees, and gardens. At the center of it all stood the grand tote board—flashing results, current odds and betting pools—proudly flanked and guarded by the Maple Leaf and the Stars and Stripes—side by side, gently fluttering in the cool autumn breeze.

By the time we had pushed back our plates, exhaled, and loosened a notch or two on our belt loops, the field for the second race had crossed the finish line. Indicating that the lot of us now needed to make our way quickly from the Club House and down four flights of escalators to the ground floor— as surely by now, the 49-ers, and Daisy of course, would be heading over from the backstretch to the saddling ring.

Already overflowing with spectators trying to get up

close and personal with the contenders for race number three, we managed to find a spot on the rail for the kids to watch and wait as Mother, Diane and I tucked under the gate, crossed over the walking ring and slipped into open stall number five.

The lineup of shanked and bridled entries began arriving minutes later, parading, and strutting their stuff around the ring before the gallery of crowded onlookers all hoping to pick the winner.

The only one little thing missing from all this thrilling pomp and pageantry, that we'd all so diligently toiled long and hard for was the damn horse!

"Where the hell could they be?" my mother nervously demanded while checking her watch and craning her head and neck up and over the backs of other horses hoping to spot Daisy and the 49-ers.

Then, unexpectedly and out of nowhere, my father suddenly appeared, pushing his way through the crowd onto the rail and yelling out in between passing horses— in that abrasive Austrian accent of his— "Margret, Ver da heil iz dat harse?"

Completely at a loss for words or an answer, Mother just threw up her arms and shrugged her shoulders.

Only seconds later, and with an exuberant expression upon his face, as if he'd spotted a bratwurst cart, my father shouted out, "Der she iz," then marched off like the *Terminator* to the outside walking ring while calling out, "I'll be back!"

As it turned out, Rob and Cindy, sensing Daisy's nervousness, had decided to veer off from the herd and take her on a guided tour of the grounds, hoping to calm her anxieties. Commendable to be sure, unfortunately, by the time my father had redirected them back to the saddling ring, the rest of the field was already tacked and mounting up to the paddock judge calling out, "Riders up."

Ultimately, we managed Daisy into the cubicle, joined by Lori and the rest of us now anxiously waiting for Mother/trainer to get the racing saddle in place and tightened up. However having to abide by the commission's rules that only the official trainer can handle the saddle before a race, Mother was now having significant difficulty adjusting the girth strap, as it was Rob who usually took care of this essential duty.

As she continued to fidget with the buckles, Daisy was becoming increasingly agitated and despite our pleading, petting and whispers to quiet down, she soon had enough, and without warning, spun around on a dime sending us all flying back against the stall wall—except for poor Rob that is.

Caught with his back to the opening and in direct line of Daisy's wielding ass, he was promptly batted and launched—homerun style— backward through the air, slam-bang onto his backside and center stage to a gaping and gasping crowd of spectators!

"Oh my gosh, Rob, are you ok?" Diane cried out as she, Lori, Cindy, and I quickly took hold of his arms—slowly and gently helping him back onto his feet.

"Ya, I'm fine," He grumbled back, slapping off, as best he could, a trouser full of dirt and manure—before returning to the imperative task of getting Daisy saddled and out to join the others in the post parade.

Finally managing the saddle, Mother gave a quick leg-up to Lori, sending horse and rider out to catch up with the others, while we managed up the children and followed the long line of foolhardy gamblers to the betting wickets.

"Twenty dollars across the board please."

With ticket now in hand, we all raced up to the second-floor balcony for an eagle-eyed view of Daisy and the others, by this time already approaching and entering the starting gate.

"They're at the post, and they're off!" Came the familiar call of the announcer's voice from the loudspeakers reverberating throughout the grandstand.

As the field broke from the gate, the children began hopping up and down and chanting, "Come on Daisy, come on Daisy."

Diane was nervously biting her nails and standing next to my mother screaming, "Get up there, come on Lori move her!"

My father was peering rather unemotionally through his antiquated binoculars, alongside the 49-ers, locked arm in arm and praying, as we all were, for a miracle, as poor Daisy was by the first turn still trailing the field.

Then seemingly as if our prayers had been heard, Lori and Daisy suddenly began moving—steadily weaving their way up through the field, around the clubhouse turn and down into the stretch now only five lengths off the pace!

At that point Diane completely lost all control of her

emotions, *entering a scream and yell frenzy* with such volume and viral intensity, that I had little doubts she'd awoken even the dead! All while a reservedly calm and quiet Rob-49 was drumming the railing tops with his rolled-up racing program—his Cindy, with rhythm, time, and great zeal, shouting and leapfrogging up onto the backs of his shoulders.

For me however, it was a bittersweet moment. Although proud and excited to see the fruits of all our labours coming to fruition, I found myself at the same time suffering a sudden sense of subtle humility. For watching Daisy strenuously battling down to the wire, at risk of life and limb, only because it had been asked of her, was a humbling and poetic reminder of those who for so long, have given us so much, so unselfishly.

Well, in the end and at the wire, we couldn't have been less than elated with the 3rd place finish. Especially given her efforts, how far she had come and not to mention that it was a first time out.

Once all the enthusiastic handshaking and high fives had subsided, the 49-ers hurriedly scrambled down to retrieve Daisy trackside—allowing the rest of us to make our way back to the backstretch to await her eventual return from test-barn— to offer her both our heartfelt congratulations and handfuls of homemade oatmeal cookies.

In the days that followed something changed in Daisy. She seemed uncommonly depleted, both physically and emotionally. Unwilling or unable to rebound back to her old tumultuous self, she instead became, even for Rob and

Cindy, quietly unapproachable— often at times standing with her head to the corner of the stall and refusing to finish her meals.

Despite several examinations that failed to reveal any injury as the cause for her condition, she steadfastly, as days turned into weeks, refused to show any improvements. Deeply concerned and utterly confused as to how to help, we finally found enlightenment one morning in Cindy's profoundly simple words.

After taking a long drag of her cigarette, and a slight pause, she then offered, "You know Martin," exhaling, "maybe this racing game just isn't her thing."

Lest they speak of troubled woes
In hallowed hearts and minds they grow
Enchained by solemn are beasts of burden
Given down to us a truth's perversion
To toil and not to seek for rest
But labour on till dying breath
Servants of eons reward ungotten
Of fallen souls that lay forgotten

Heeding to words of wisdom, Diane and I, and eventually even Mother, had to admit that perhaps we'd all had a pretty good kick at the can. So, the decision was made to retire one short-lived racing stable and its golden girl down into the annals of racing history.

Under the advice and suggestion of Rob and Cindy, who reminded us of Daisy's propensity and talent for clearing railings, we made arrangements for her at the equestrian center were the 49-ers spent their afternoons—so as that they could oversee her retraining to work with children as a showjumper.

For many years after that we kept in regular touch with Rob and Cindy, who reported to our delight, that Daisy had not only returned to her rackety old self, but had amassed a string of show ribbons and was to the staff and students the favourite in the barn.

The Five of Diamonds

By the time we had organized, assembled, and loaded our chairs, tackle, lunch and iceboxes onto the wagon, all of tissue, toilet and tail had been merrily forgotten. That being the case, it wasn't long before we were wheeling our way out through the forest hollow, down along the fence line, and off to my dear Diane's picnic at the pond.

"Howdy neighbour!" came the all-too-familiar greeting from Jamie and his wife Bobby as we passed by next door. And for a moment we paused to shoot the breeze with these kind folks who, as repayment for all of the entertainment we had been recently providing them, had graciously permitted us to fish for the annual stocking of trout that they managed at the pond.

True outdoorsmen in every sense of the word—she in her baseball cap and checkered flannel lumber jacket and he in a camouflage coat and fluorescent hat—were busy preparing their yard for yet another season of campfires and cookouts. A lifelong passion that rest assured left neither friend nor foe, nor fish or fowl safe when the season came calling. Hardly passed a day when salmon wasn't smoking, venison wasn't hanging, or the fallen feathers of feathered friends weren't lofting through the air.

As if to illustrate my very point, one fine morning in the last of the past September, Jamie had unexpectedly appeared at our front door brandishing high two plucked and prepared bags of birds.

"Here ya go neighbour, had extra!"

"What are they?" I asked.

"Canadian geese, ever had one? They're delicious!"

"Ah, no, not really," chuckling, "can't say that I have, where did you get them?"

"Dropped them as they flew overhead the house yesterday."

"Oh, ok, thanks, Jamie."

"No problem, neighbour."

Zahra, finally having had enough of all the neighbourly chitter- chatter that morning by the fence line, began meowing, chirping, and brushing herself up against my shins, indicating it was now time to move along.

And so with a final wave, we slowly began to lose sight of our red-necked neighbours, calling out only a last word of caution though the cups of their palms, "Watch out for the Koi!"— reminding us kindly to avoid hooking the beautifully coloured carp that they'd been so dedicatedly training to feed at the shoreline.

Pondside, Diane popped open the beach chairs and perfectly placed them on each side of the picnic basket beneath the shade of a large sun umbrella. Rummaging through her bags, she extracted out a large plastic bowl that she promptly filled to the rim with pretzels, cheese doodles and chips. All set and ready, she then cracked a cold can of cola, plunked herself down, sloughed her feet up onto the drink cooler and began leafing through the pictured pages of those ridiculous Hollywood trash magazines that she is so fond of.

Zahra, taking advantage of the sluggish bugs not yet fully charged up by the heat of the morning sun, began busying herself by stalking, apprehending, and assembling a considerable collection of jumping, flying and creeping crawlies.

A few dozen yards or so, down and around the embankment, I had settled on a large grassy knoll that provided a high vantage point over the water's edge — splashed with a healthy helping of reeds and rushes that I felt undoubtedly was the spot from which to cast in a line.

Becoming excited at the prospect of contributing a trout or two into Zahra's cache of creatures, I enthusiastically unlatched and opened my tackle box, that much like a child's pop-up picture book, spread out the multi-tiered trays of precious cargo hidden inside.

As I began to sort through the treasured rows of hooks, jigs, spoons and spinners, one in particular, attracted my attention. Glistening and gleaming in the sunshine of the morning, I could see my distorted reflection in the concave of its silver side. Careful not to become ensnared onto the barbs of its dangerously trebled hook, I rightly tinkered and toyed it over, pondering for a moment at the gold and red tetragon markings that had made it infamously known to serious anglers as *The Five of Diamonds.*

Nearly the span of my hand, this sinister sized spoon was by no means a lure for pond trout. But rather a masterful illusion, crafted and created for the precarious allurement of the real monsters lurking deep in the depths of the most revered angling waters in Canada—Muskellunge, big Lakers, Walleye, and of course, the Northern Pikes or Jack as they are called by the Dene people that we spent almost a year teaching and living with on the shores of the mighty Lake Athabasca!

Incredible, I reflected, looking beyond the lure in my hand to Diane and Kitten, tittering at the edge of the pond beyond, realizing that it had been all but twenty years since we had ventured far up into the vast hinterlands of Northern Saskatchewan—and just as long since the very day I last cast the Five of Diamonds out into the waters of Athabasca, in hopes of a first prize catch in the annual Fond-du-Lac fishing derby.

Talk of the big event and the prize money was already buzzing and echoing around the village by the time the five of us and all our gear had been successfully delivered from the airfield— via the back of a pickup truck—to our new accommodations on the cul-de-sac of teacher's housing. A neighbourhood of well- constructed single and two-story homes that would now serve as temporary lodgings for the diversely eclectic mix of teachers, who with or without families, had all come together from across Canada to do our thing.

At the forefront of our welcoming committee was a

pretty young girl of maybe twelve or thirteen, with coal-black hair, lovely Asian eyes and a brimming wide smile, who after loudly rapping several times at the front door inquired of me, "I drink water?"

"Pardon me?" I replied, a little unsure of what she was requesting. Her smile broadened, then again, "I drink water?"

"I'm sorry, what is your name?"

"Wanita."

"So, I drink water?"

From a nearby porch, an as yet unacquainted colleague feeling the need to interject yelled over, "She wants to know if you'll give her a glass of water."

"Oh, ok, thanks."

"Sure Wanita, just a sec."

Returning with a glass, she then took a few sips, handed it back with an affirmative "Marci Cho", and then promptly demanded, "We come in now?"

Glancing back to her delegation of fellow committee members, idling at the foot of the steps, but seemingly ready and raring to go, and not wanting to start relations by acting impolitely, I happily offered them to come inside for a brief meet and greet with our family.

"I wouldn't have done that!" A little bird leaning on the rails of the deck next store suddenly cried out.

In hindsight, I'd wished I'd gotten the do's and don'ts of village etiquette a few seconds sooner—as this little band of holy terrors, forthwith and without hesitation, began recklessly ransacking their way through every box, bag, cupboard and closet in the house—hysterically laughing and callously tossing about even our most private things, that included but were not limited to, Diane's scanty bras and undies.

"Ok guys, that's enough!" Diane and I tried to reason and settle the little hellions down. This only caused them just to laugh louder, scurrying and scampering up the stairs, cluster bouncing and trampolining from one bed to the next.

Swiftly and speedily overstaying their welcome, but resolutely refusing to leave, we eventually had no choice but to wrangle, wrestle and capture the little darlings, one-by-one, and deliver them squirming under-arm back and out the front door.

By the time we had repaired the house, shelved Diane's undergarments, unpacked and packed away our luggage, washed up and redressed the children and then sat them down to a hearty bowl of soup and sandwiches, there came yet another knock at the door.

"Oh boy, not again?" I mumbled as I made my way to see who it was now.

To my relief, it wasn't a redeployment of pint-sized thugs, but rather in fact a small company of adult welcome wishers.

Leading the introductions, was a slightly heavyset man, clearly in his thirties but curiously sporting wisps of grey throughout his flops of black hair atop a handsome moustache attached to goatee.

"Hi, Martin?"

"Yes," I replied with a firm handshake.

"My name is Lewis, head of the computer lab and tech

studies. This is Lance, an elementary teacher from Edmonton, and this beautiful lady is my wife Cathy, a nurse at the Med-Station"—clutching pridefully onto his wholesomely attractive spouse, who herself was cradling an infant in one arm, a welcome basket in the other and a toddler clenching at the pleats of her pants beside her.

"Oh, and my two children, Mathew and down there, somewhere around here is Rebecca."

As Diane then joined us at the door, I took a moment to allow for reintroductions, providing Cathy with an opportunity to present to us a welcome basket jam-packed with pints of hand-picked wild blueberries, homemade pies and cookies.

"Wow, that's so kind of you," Diane poured over the items in the basket. "Would you like to come in for a tea or coffee?"

And as the ladies and children moved into the kitchen for teatime, the men pushed out onto the porch with cold drinks to get better acquainted. Whereupon I must admit that I already had Lewis at a distinctive disadvantage, on account of his easily recognizable Newfoundlander accent, that to the fullest extent broadcasted without question a *born and raised East Coaster*.

Largely descended from Irish migrants in search of a better life, the people of Newfoundland and Labrador are well known across Canada for their persistent jovial spirit, a sarcastic wit, a willingness to speak their minds and, not unlike their Irish cousins, having what it takes to drink anyone else under the table. Especially if that involves swigging back a twenty-sixer or two of the notoriously infamous *Newfie Screech*.

As if to cleverly call him out on his pedigree, I smugly smirking suggested, "So where are you from Lewis, St John's?"

Without missing a step, he volleyed right back with *a-lotta bit of Newfinese*. "Yes by, I dare say. Where y' longs to? Maybe we ought put the ol' slut on, some wood in da 'ole and ave a yarn bout it eh?"

Directly on the other side of me, and of the coin, was Lance. A staunchly proud Albertan, leaning on a heritage of rural-hardened central European pioneers, who had been recruited by the provincial government of the day, in hopes that their skills, determination and courage might tame the Prairies—and who, after centuries of hardship, had forged and carved out a Western culture alongside their American mid-west neighbors that was celebrated annually at the world-famous Calgary Stampede!

Perhaps ten years our senior and slightly humble in stature, Lance, toggling his 70's era glasses and gear, had a uniquely provocative practice of contrasting his mild-mannered image by firing off one-line zingers whenever the opportunity presented itself.

True to his form and style, he bantered back at Lewis. "St. John's eh? You know, I recently heard about three fellas that drove down from the east coast to visit Martin here in Toronto."

Lewis began to smile, anticipating the gag.

"But when they got close and saw a big sign on the

highway that read *Toronto Left,* they turned around and went back home."

"Ya, that's a good one there Lance...but let me tell ya what the problem is. You Albertans are just too obvious."

Still humoured by his own joke, Lance sniggered back.

"Oh, how's that?"

"Well, for example, we can always tell when you guys are married."

"Why's that?" Lance requested

"Cause the chewing tobacco stains are on both sides of the truck."

As I chuckled, hiding my face to the floor, Lewis paused to knock back the last of his drink, then glancing over my shoulder at our rods leaning against the railing put forth, "Fancy yourself a bit of a fisherman do ya, Marty? Thinking about maybe entering the Derby tomorrow, are ya?"

Feeling the need to mark my own spot onto our collective geographical map, I boasted back, "Well, ya, sure, because as you know, back home in Ontario we have some of the best fishing waters in Canada."

Instantly, as if I'd landed a perfect snare and cymbal punchline, Lewis turned away his head, trumpeting out a mouthful of drink, while Lance belly-ached away on the other side. Looking back and forth at each of them and puzzled by all the jocularity, I inquired, "What's funny about that?"

"Sorry Martin," Lance, taking a breath, "No offence but we don't often meet a Torontonian who knows too much about fishing!"

"Ya," Lewis added. "I'm afraid you're just a little too far west of the Maritimes for that Marty."

Feeling a little westerly-insulted himself, Lance batted back, "Well, we're not talking about netting cod here Lewis. Let's not forget I've got home advantage and when it comes to outwitting the big Jack, well sorry to say, but you boys don't stand a chance!"

"Tell ya what," Lewis began to announce while setting his drink down decisively onto the railing, "I've got a boat rented for tomorrow's Derby, and I'll' bet each of ya *two weeks yard duty* I get the best of the bunch if not outright win the contest!"

"I'll take that bet," Lance shot back, offering his hand to seal the deal.

"You in Marty?"

"Ya sure, ok Lewis, but if only you'll promise to please stop calling me Marty."

Well, once the territorial, *slash- fish-pissing-match* had ended and Diane had laid down with the children for a little rest, I decided I'd best saddle up, get my game face on and go out and test the waters.

Thereupon, having secured my trusted tried and true Red Devil spoon onto the leader and line, I excitely headed out toward town and for the shores of the mighty Athabasca.

Just beyond the top edge of the hillside, or uptown as it were, I soon stumbled upon the most spectacular view of the village lying perilously at the foot of the enormous lake below. Panoramically humbled, I required a moment to fully take in and appreciate the incredible vast expanse of Boreal, that even by early September had already begun to lay a blanket of gold across the endless scenery.

A sudden chill in the air then caused me to consider what now loomed ominously just beyond the distant horizon—mere shadows of daylight creeping out from beneath a torrent of long, dark and cold winter nights.

How many unremembered souls, I began to wonder, had lived and died here? Persisting and enduring through the centuries of struggle and strife, unaided by those things that we take so for granted—only to lay buried in the icy graves of this remote and unforgiving land.

Unexpectedly, but deliciously moved by the moment, I found myself fondly reminiscing a familiar ode of verse to the trials of Sam McGee:

"Talk of your cold! Through the parka's fold, it stabbed like a driven nail. If our eyes we'd close, then the lashes froze till sometimes we couldn't see."

— ROBERT W. SERVICE

The sacred ground on which Fond du Lac was built, from the French meaning *Bottom of the Lake, had* suffered many unfortunate years of bloody conflict between the Chipewyan and the European explorers who arrived here in hopes of expanding commerce. After massacres, wars and unrelenting bloodshed, the pioneers eventually abandoned the area, only to be reclaimed and resettled by the Denesulin First Nation nearly one hundred and fifty years ago. And as I ambled along and down onto the village street, it soon became apparent that the spirits and the sordid history of the land still strongly resonate within the culture and people who live here.

The gravel-dry road was flanked on one side by an unordered assortment of tired cabins and cottages, each boasting a small stick-picket fence around it. Intermittently, a four-wheeled bike would motor by, commonly piloted by a young woman and her brood clinging on and clutching bags of goods from the trading post—lofting plumes of dust upon me and the little litters of raggle-taggle pups wandering aimlessly about the camp.

On the far side of the street stood a line of public buildings, including the Band office, the Police barracks, the Northern Store, and of course, Father Gamache Memorial School. Not in the least what I might have expected, this impressive building, while perhaps a little overdressed for the occasion, was an elegant design of simple sophistication. Adorned with a collection of cobalt blue metallic canopies perched elegantly atop stone walls of function and form, it was equal to or even grander than many of the schools in the urban centers below.

With pole in hand, I stood for a minute or two, lingering upon my impending tenure, before suddenly finding myself encircled, and effectively ambushed by a barely in their teens band of blabbering boys—and, not to my surprise, Wanita, who I presumed had quickly rounded up and organized the entire posse the minute she saw me leaving the house.

Promptly abandoning her precocious ear to ear smile,

and like a parent scolding a badly-behaved child, she would nearly yell at me, "You're my teacher you know!"

"How do you know that Wanita?" I asked quietly in return, trying to calm her intensity.

"How do I know?" She shouted at me with a look of disbelief at my ignorance. "I looked at the class list, how can you not know that teacher?"

Trying not to laugh too hard, I replied, "Well Wanita, I just got here you know."

Redirecting the conversation suddenly to himself, the captain of the troop, introducing himself as Christopher, while not forgetting his first lieutenant as Jeffery, began tugging at the locks dangling at my shoulders.

"Blonde hair eh? And blue eyes uh?"

"Yes," pushing his pointed finger away from my face. "Don't you like blue eyes, Christopher?"

Sternly and decisively he returned, "No, I don't!" Scanning my accoutrements, he then demanded, "You want to go fishing?"

"No, Christopher, I just like to carry around a fishing rod for good luck."

"You think you're funny?" Wanita barked at me.

Turning my smirk from Wanita back to Christopher, I queried, "Well then young man, can you tell me where a good place is to throw in a line?"

Looking back at me as if I were utterly daft, he simply waved his arm along the entire length of shoreline, plainly declaring, "Anywhere!" —causing his full company to break into a burst of hearty laughter while slapping, punching, poking each other and chattering on in their native Dene.

"Follow me teacher!" Jeffery broke in to save the day, ordering his men to take up camp and head off for a secret spot by the lake. Tipping my cap to Wanita, who had decided to leave the business of the hunt to the men, I eagerly took up chase behind my gang of giggling guides, down a path through the forest and out to a small clearing that suddenly exposed the foreboding waters of an inland sea.

As I steadied and readied myself and the reel at a promising point of the shoreline, my new mates took up position atop a large rocky outcrop, squatting down and preparing themselves to be at very least amused.

First cast—strike! "Wow!" I shouted out, prompting laughter from the gallery. My rod nervously bent right over, the line straining as the reel struggled and strived to wind out the drag before the force of the fish snapped the wire.

For not too short a time, I laboured through the process of reel and release, slowly tiring my opponent, until finally kicking off my shoes and stepping ankle-deep into the water, I managed to ease and cradle it up onto the shore.

"Ha!" Check that out boys! Must be a twenty pounder, wow!" And, entirely elated with myself, I proceeded to carefully remove the hook from the jack's jowls and slowly slide him back into the sea.

"Why you do that?" Christopher shouted out, visibly annoyed, and confused.

"What?"

"Why you let it go?"

Equally confused, I replied, "I just fish for the fun of it, then release them."

"Ah!" He cried out, waving his hand at me, "You fish for nothing!"

Second cast, same as the first. "Unbelievable," I hollered at myself, simply having the angler's time of my life. However, this time around demanding that I refrain from wasting valuable resources, Christopher insisted that instead I turn over to him the spoils of my labour.

Taking it from me with a dry, contorted droll-like expression on his face, he and the boys then quickly assembled a batch of firewood, lit and blew it to a flame, formed a cross-legged circle around it and then spit my fish onto a stick.

Minutes later, as the fire crackled and they chattered and chuckled along, they began to pick and pull at a perfectly grilled feast that left me understandably introspecting, *who here was the student and who were the teachers.*

Nevertheless, the following morning as the sun broke quietly over the edge of the horizon and the last remnants of mist danced about the still of surface, the three of us anxiously headed out in search of the real colossus, the goliaths of the deep and the terrifying titans that tempted our imaginations.

And as we slid over the summer ice towards the mouth of Grease Bay, I couldn't help but feel a sense of sin as our craft unsettled the glittering calm of the restful waters.

But when we finally eased alongside the towering stone cliffs that shaded the eastern shoreline, our collective attentions were quickly and intently refocused to the business at hand.

Manning the engine from the stern of the ship, Lewis, feeling our position was now in perfect line with the rock wall, affirmatively gave the order to "drop all lines," officially signaling the commencement of the competition.

Lance, with his back to the bow of our sixteen-foot skiff, called out, "I'm going right," casting out a foot-long Rapala to near the end of a mile of line.

Midship, I announced, "Cliffside," slamming a hefty Williams Wabler off the stone face and deep down into the drink below.

"Ok boys, I'm off the back then," called out our captain, releasing behind a massive red and silver spinner, that was quite nearly the size of Labrador.

All went quiet, save the subtle idle of the engine, as we slowly trolled along with great anticipation. And for a moment, one had to fully appreciate the immense scope of nature that, in every way, captivated your very consciousness—tempered however, by an ill at ease sense of transience to the powers of creation that precariously seemed to cradle our very own existence. An experience that brought to me an deeper appreciation for the famous twentieth-century natural enthusiasts Jackson, Carmichael and Tom Thompson to name only a few of the renowned Group of Seven, who came to leave their legacy by painting the incredible landscapes of Canada's true north.

"Fish on!" Lewis shrieked, springing to his feet with

such impetuous velocity as to launch himself quite nearly out from the boat—before spinning around, shutting down the motor and asking all lines in, so as not to entangle the operation. Unified within the excitement of the moment, that easily overshadowed our competitive spirits, Lance and I quickly stowed away our rods and made ready the net.

"She's big boys, got some serious weight and diving for the bottom," reporting back to his shipmates. However, his intonations were growing ever uneasy, as the spool of his reel was steadily winding away, down to the very end of the line!

To his credit, Lewis skillfully played the last of the spider wire perfectly, steadily regaining the advantage. After nearly twenty minutes of heated battle, the beleaguered creature finally began to reveal itself, slowly emerging out from within the dark depths below.

"I think it's a huge lake trout Lewis"—whispering to near the end of my breath, as I teetered over the gunwales of the ship to get a closer look.

"Lance, pass me the net!" then diving it deep into the water and beneath the beast. As Lewis strained to pull him ever higher, I was finally able to slide the speckled silver giant into the mesh!

Yet despite the immensity of this beautiful creature, Lewis commanded, "Big, but not big enough boys, let him go."

"But he's huge Lewis," I argued back.

"Not huge enough Marty. Not for these parts!"

A statement of fact that effectively realigned our

collective understanding of what it was that we were actually in search of.

After several more false starts and false hopes had been returned and released, we eventually came across an immense pool of water churning and swirling at the foot of a large waterfall.

"This will be a good spot," Lance insisted. "Deep, Walleye will be down there, and our boy will be around here somewhere hunting them."

Too deep for our anchor, Lewis did his best to steady the boat as it turned and twisted about in the turmoil of the currents beneath.

Feeling a sudden sense of palpable premonition, I reached for the *Five of Diamonds* and quickly fastened it to my line. Hurriedly casting out to near the base of the falls, I sent the bait skipping once or twice across the surface before letting it tumble down to the depths of the pool, surreptitiously disguised as an injured and vulnerable prey. Then, ever so slowly, I gave a gentle turn of the reel, and a scant tug of the rod to tantalizingly bring it back to life.

And then all hell broke loose!

The force at which my rod slammed down onto the hull was incredible. The tip was bending right over and down into the water and the reel was screaming as Lewis shouted out, "Martin, tighten the drag or he'll run you right out of line— not that tight, not that tight, it'll snap!"

"Lance, look out, duck!" I hollered out at him as the monster suddenly swung around the boat, dragging the straining line across the bow and nearly decapitating the poor man in the process.

"He's making a run for the channel opening," Lewis shouted, desperately trying to turn about and steer the vessel to keep after him.

"Lewis," I nervously called back, "I can see the end of the spool!"

"Give it here, quick!" Lance demanded, insisting that he could stretch himself and the rod out over the bow, giving the precious inches needed to save the day.

Teetering nearly at the end of his limits, all suddenly stopped, offering a momentary calm that seemed to signal that perhaps the battle was now turning in our favour.

"Shoot, that was close eh?" Lance lofted back at us, beginning to reel, when just as sudden a lurch of the great fish violently yanked him forward, sending him flying off the front of the boat headfirst into and beneath the surface of the water!

"Oh no Lewis!" I sprang to the edge in hopes of a rescue, but to my distress, he was nowhere to be found! "Oh my goodness Lewis, he's gone under the boat, I think he's gone under the boat."

Fearing the unthinkable, we struggled with what to do when, thankfully and suddenly he resurfaced—panic paddling, gasping, hacking and unbelievably not only still in possession of his glasses, but more importantly, the fishing rod as well.

"Lance!" I yelled lunging and draping over the boat's hull while quickly clasping him by the collar of his jacket. Clenching the arms of his misted bifocals in the grip of my teeth, I relayed the rod to Lewis before then giving all I had to desperately reinstall him into the boat. But far to saturated and weighted down with water was he for this to succeed without putting the entire little craft in jeopardy of capsizing.

"We'll just tow him to the shoreline," Lewis insisted. "Hang on to him!"

Quickly beaching the boat, we scrambled up and over the edge of the hull onto the rocky slope, carefully coordinating our efforts to heave and haul our soggy and waterlogged comrade out from the water and securely back onto dry land.

Coughing and choking out the last drops of lake water from his lungs, he cried out, "Where's the bloody rod?"

Suddenly realizing that in our haste to salvage our pal, we had foolishly left the pole lying upon the gunnel. Quickly we dashed back to the boat, but to little avail, as we arrived seconds too late and only in time to witness the distressingly awful sight of it being drawn and levered over the edge of the scow and now surely away to a timeless grave at the bottom of the lake.

But like a man possessed, and without concern for his safety, as if he were transforming into Superman, Lewis tore away his glasses, ripped open his jacket and dove fists first down into the depths— heroically risking life and limb, in a desperate bid to retrieve and redeem for our crew the last chance for a prize in the Derby!

. . .

"MARTIN...MARTIN!"ABRUPTLY breaking my thoughts and attracting my attention away from my reflections.

"Hun, look!" Diane whispered as loud as she possibly could while pointing down to the edge of the pond.

"The koi fish are here," excited at the arrival of Jamie's fishy stock, richly adorned with beautiful red and gold markings.

"Be careful Di, the bank is muddy and slippery," I warned back while hurriedly closing up my hooks and tackle, so as that I could head around and have a peek for myself.

Mindful of her footing, Diane slowly reached down to open the lid of the picnic basket, quickly and quietly extracting several slices of bread and began to pick and toss bits for the accumulating collection of koi.

Zahra, having caught eye of this mouth-watering new development, immediately abandoned her bug hunt, and took up position alongside Diane at the water's edge.

"Look Hun, there are even more arriving out now," Diane laughed out loud, while excitedly encouraging the conglomeration of carp by donating and doling out the last of our precious sandwiches.

Caught up in the excitement of all this swishing and swashing about, Zahra began to patter and paw at the little lips, fins and whiskers, teasing just beyond her reach. Then, for whatever her reasons, likely overwhelmed by her instincts, she bounded out from the shoreline, and much like Lewis, went pouncing paws and headfirst deep into the pond.

"Oh no, Zahra!" Diane screamed out, jumping up and

down with her hands on her head, inadvertently shaking and shifting lose her delicate foundation quickly causing it to give way, sending her slowly sliding down the muddy slope and surely into the lagoon.

"Oh, crap!" I dropped my gear and raced around the edge of the pool to try and save my poor spouse, now frantically wind milling and backstroking her arms trying desperately to avoid a polar plunge into the pond. But it was too late, as before I could arrive to assist, her feet slipped out forward hurling her down onto her back, arms stretched out above her head and gliding now like a grand ship being launched straight into the tank!

Like synchronized swimmers, Kitten and my consort's heads popped out, sequentially cat-paddling back toward the boggy shoreline, dividing and dispersing the school of koi along their way.

Rummaging frantically around the ground, I found a dried- out stick of tree branch with a hefty crook that I thought would make a good rescue pole and hook. Dashing back to the pond, where nimble Kitten had already managed to beach herself, I extended out the wand to my wife—to you know, to save her life!

"Diane, don't yank like that, you're going to pull me in too, just go easy," I begged her to calm down.

"I can't get up, it's too slippery, ah... it's freezing, help me!"

For a few seconds we played tug of war with our tones and the twiggy timber before, as one would expect, I lost my own precious footing, effectively launching me and the bloody rescue stick right into the ice-cold reservoir as well!

Well, you can imagine for yourself the flabbergasted faces of the elderly couple, who at that very moment, chanced by while walking their dog—confounded no doubt to understand why Diane and I were paddling around the icy pond, fully dressed in the middle of May, screaming at each other like a couple of idiots!

Smartly, he unleashed their tubby little Beagle and tossed us in one end of the line. Then extending out the retractable contraption some fifteen feet or so, he firmly anchored himself on the high and dry ground. With his wife now bear-hugging him about the waist, they managed to haul our sorry soaked asses slowly but successfully out of the water.

Thanking us for the good laugh, and no doubt a tale to tell the neighbourhood when they got home, they kept along while Diane and I, shivering and shaking, packed and wrapped up our crap, our soggy cat and squished our way back for home.

Passing back by Jamie and Bobby, still working far away in their yard, he called out to us, "Back so soon, neighbour?"

"Yup," I quivered back.

Leaning and grinning on her rake, Bobby added in, "Did ya see any koi?"

"Sure did," Diane offered back. "Up close and personal as a matter of fact!"

Zahra's Saree

Preoccupied as we were, with all the silly goings-on in our silly empty nest, Diane and I hadn't taken notice that for some time now we'd been covertly being watch—rather inconspicuously I might add, by an odd couple and their three children, who had been participating for many years in our soccer programs. And as it so happened, and as soon we would come to discover, they were now preparing to approach us with a "proposal of partnership," hoping as they were, to cut themselves a slice of our soccer pie.

I distinctly remember that this all started on the very day marking Zahra's ninth month with us—duly noted, as the exhibition of my dear wife merrily singing "happy anniversary" to our cat, while presenting to her nine miniature custard-covered-buttercups with nine miniature unlit candles on top, was not something soon to be forgotten.

Nonetheless, post sugar rush breakfast, we headed out together early that Saturday morning in the last week of August, to help organize and supervise the annual awards day and ceremonies for our soccer leagues— and as yet unbeknown to us our first *formal* encounter with *Sony and Cher.*

Of East Indian descent, but born and raised in Toronto, Doron and his wife Annie, (anglicized somehow from Parveen), were entirely atypical to the influx of Indian emigrants driving the rapid expansion of communities in the Greater Toronto Area. Despite a committed, albeit bipartisan participation in their family's faith and traditions, they were as we soon would discover, as Canuck as a Canuck could be.

Doron, a man of modest height, bearing a tawny complexion, dark circles and a noticeably coloured-crop of jet-black hair, began immediately to convey to me, in not so many words, a passion surprisingly not for soccer but rather for hockey— and more specifically the disappointingly unsuccessful Toronto Maple Leaf's Organization. Who then went further on to startle and stun both Diane and I by tossing out bouts of profanity riddled criticisms at me as comfortably as if we had been long since twinned at birth. Case in point, while making our pre-proposition small talk, field side beneath a large umbrella, and arguing as I was the merits of soccer over hockey, he proceeded to ask me, amid his laughter, "What are you, some kind of fucking idiot?"

Rest assured, had this come barreling out from anyone else, it would have been dukes-up! —but this little brown man had a uniquely derived capacity to launch cussword put-downs in a way that could bemuse the recipient into believing that they were, in fact, actually meant as terms of endearment.

To Doron's compliment however was his wife Annie. Proud to a fault of her Mauritian descendancy and fluent in French Creole, she was equally unique to her counterpart but in an entirely different way. Cultured and absolutely brimming with self-confidence, Annie's claim to fame, as it eventually became apparent, was to dependably arrive decked out to the nines in an ensemble of rigging, on par or better than that of the most notable Hollywood hotties.

Her attractive expression, slightly more Arabic than Indian, beautifully complimented a slender build and prodigiously bounding breast-line—which provided a perfect framework for building the bombshell!

A thick thatch of bottle blonde mane gently cascaded down to and alongside a slightly exposed and diamond-studded mid-drift. Hinting at her inner magnetism but tastefully concealing and cloaking it behind a well-appointed *attirement* of Saint Laurent tops, Armani jeans and stiletto-heeled Gucci's.

Yet despite all this grandiose theatricality, it quickly became apparent that lying beneath the surface was a genuinely kind and kindred spirit—who immediately began to dazzle us with not only her boisterous personality and infectious laughter, but to my delight, an involuntary tendency to publicly scold and chastise her husband!

"Doron you moron, what the hell are you talking about?"—shaking her head with frustration while turning to Diane and me, and with a half-smile firmly affirming, "you see what I have to deal with on a daily basis!"

Unharmed, Doron would just laugh it off and continue *chin-wagging* on about the characters in Shrek or some other trivial and non- related to our soccer-conference material.

Curiously entertaining as this meeting of minds was, as minutes turned into hours we soon began to see that quite remarkably a kinship of sorts was taking hold—and so, by the close of the day we all decided to move and continue our conversations and deliberations on and into the dining room of our favourite steak house—The Keg!

Famishedly seated around the table, the four of us began mulling and musing over the menu, and despite our common fluency in Canuckian *ehs*, loonies, toques and toonies, a pinch of cultural disparities began to emerge— which unforeseeably would soon have the most ridiculously outrageous implications, not for us, but of all things our dear sweet Zahra!

"Good evening folks." our host kindly introduced himself. "Before we get started, can I get everyone something to drink?"

Feeling obliged to speak for the group, as I suggested the restaurant, I politely asked, "would you guys like red or white wine with your dinner?"

Doron lowering his menu and peeking over his bifocals teetering at the edge of his nose, humbly replied, "Oh, sorry, we don't drink alcohol, it's against our religion."

As he continued on then requesting a ginger ale for himself and a cranberry-tonic for Annie, it occurred to me, what is a beautiful steak dinner without a glass of Chianti, Merlot or Malbec?—surely as senseless as a dog-less dog, a butter-less cob or still worse, a cheeseless plate of mac... Imagine that!

Kicking at my shins under the table, in an effort to knock the glazed expression from my face, Diane then rang in with, "Hey Annie, if you're thinking starters, I suggest the bacon-wrapped scallops, they are to die for!"

"I'm sure they are, but unfortunately, we can't have pork either, it is against our religion too."

Still grappling and reeling with the notion of alcohol-free, I honestly had to draw the philosophical line at the prospect of living life without bacon.

But of course understanding that multiculturalism had become the cornerstone of our new nation—and being respectful of the age-old adage, to each his own—we continued on enthusiastically ripping into a fresh loaf of sourdough bread while listening to Annie as she began to summarize the advantages of a partnership. Talking about their community connections, their experience with online marketing and a willingness to spearhead the havoc-infested frontlines of field management, she was making some good points.

"This would allow you and Diane to step back behind the scenes and take a more relaxed, administrative role in the business."

I heard that! And adding to all of this, a significant injection of capital investment—the plan, from where I was sitting, was starting to look rather good!

Pleased with how the presentation was going, Annie

paused for a moment to butter herself up a slice of bread, giving Doron, who had been silent up until then, an opportunity to interject and add to the discussion his own two cents.

Clearing his throat with a sip of ginger ale, he asked, "Hey Martin, did you know that Eddie Murphy was the voice of Donkey in the Shrek movies?"

"Doron, you dolt," Annie shrieked out across the table at him. "What are you talking about?"

For several minutes, the dressing-down and effective emasculation of her poor perplexed husband continued on until a trio of wait staff mercifully arrived with our meals.

"Careful folks, the plates are very hot!" Delivering down unto each of us a delightful culinary display of mixed greens, twice mashed potatoes, and perfectly aged beef tenderloin.

As our garcon fiercely twisted the final twist of his yard-long peppermill, there came suddenly to the table a disturbing waling, a man's voice wailing and bellowing out from the depths of Annie's purse.

"What the hell is that?" I blurted out.

Struggling with the zipper, "Oh sorry, that's my call to prayer alarm."

"Your what?"

"My call to prayer alarm." Continuing to wrestle with her handbag, she eventually managed to free her phone, effectively compounding the volume to the point where it had managed to silence the entire dining room. Now quickly stepping up and back from the table, they announced that they would return in a few moments.

"Where are you going?" Diane asked.

"We have to go out to the car and pray."

"Your supper will get cold!" I added.

"We won't be long; besides, I have to send my steak back," Doron complained.

"Why what's wrong with it?"

"The tenderloin has bacon wrapped around it."

"Why don't you just remove it?"

"The steak will still have bacon juice on it."

"Oh," I replied.

Well, while Diane and I were awaiting the return of the praying Bono's and Sonny's pork-pulled-refried-beef, we began to discuss the possible pitfalls and potential windfalls of a partnering.

Agreeing that we needed a little more time to digest and consider, we suggested to Doron and Annie, as they reseated themselves at the table, that "Perhaps you two should come up to our house next Saturday for lunch, so as that we might outline and possibly nail down the specifics for an agreement?"

"That would be awesome," Annie answered back while checking her schedule. "Hmm... we do have a cultural event that morning, but if you don't mind," chuckling, "us showing up in our suits and sarees, we'd love to come— besides, my cousins are dying to meet you guys."

Cousins?

"Sure, no problem, what should we make?"

"Oh, that's ok, it's our custom to bring our own food— and anyway our friends and family only eat halal meat."

"Halal?"

"Ya, the animal has to be slaughtered a certain way, it's part of our religion. Would that be ok with you?"

"Sure," I giggled, after all what could be better than an all- expenses-paid, self-catered, and alcohol-free saree-soiree?

Over coffee and desserts, while Doron and I debated the future of the hapless Leafs, Annie and Diane poured over pictures of the elegant and elaborately coloured sarees traditionally worn by the women of not only India but around the world.

"Look at these Martin, aren't they beautiful?" — redirecting my attention to a scroll of stunning dresses blazon with blends of cobalt, gold and emerald palatially weaving around the beautiful women wearing them. Complimenting the ensemble, a graceful and refined drapery slung calmly over a delicate arm and richly, nearly opulently, flowing down to its final fringe— and the unseen crack hiding dangerously beneath the ice—*a string of tassels.*

The following Saturday, as the heavens spat lightly down upon us and the cuckoo bird in our cuckoo clock had twice cuckooed, Diane called out to me from the front door window.

"Martin, come and take a look at this."

"Good grief," I began to whisper for no particularly good reason. "I took 'cousins and us' to mean, maybe one car of five people, not one car of five people plus two fully loaded mini-vans!"

As we spied from behind glass a baker's dozen or so of brightly costumed characters began exiting their vehicles

— promptly busying themselves with the task of loading up onto each other bowls upon bowls of cellophane wrapped, I presumed, curried concoctions.

Once all were stacked, packed, presented and accounted for, the entire clan quickly queued up, lockstep in and behind their grand marshal Annie— who with a blast of her whistle and the signal to charge, began leading the prismatic precession, like the Mahatma himself, down along our winding walkway.

Marshaling her colourful cavalcade in a ravishingly red coral and silver saree, teeming with gold bangles and dripping with white pearls, Annie utterly eclipsed her humble husband— meekly tagging behind, clad in his Aladdin pajamas, curly toed shoes and a pillbox hat. Nonetheless, entrusted as he was, with the rather imperial duty of tightrope-navigating, without fail or fall, two large trays of halal chicken to the kitchen from the car.

As the caravan neared the front steps, Diane and I swung open the door to cordially greet and receive our company. Completely forgetting about Zahra, who likely concluding that the incoming train of jewel-twinkling, tassel-trailing rainbowed sarees were just a line of walking Christmas trees for her amusement —sprang with great eagerness out onto the front step to have a closer look.

I have to tell you, the unholy shrieking and screaming that ensued was not to be believed. I'm talking, horror-filled, terror stricken, Vishnu's angry face popping out from the clouds screaming as if I had leapt from the house donning a hockey mask and wielding a revving chainsaw at them!

Dumbfounded and at a loss to understand how or why this was happening— as no one had yet informed us that many Indian people have an inherent fear of cats— I yelled and pleaded back, "Annie, she won't hurt you!"

Failing to quiet the riot, I stepped out and quickly bent down to pick up and stow away Kitten. Of course, Kitten, engaged and empowered by all the commotion, as one would expect, simply skipped ahead of my grasp and down a step closer to the huddled mass of petrified strangers.

Annie, now panic-stricken, as if a Bengal tiger had lurched out from the high grass, instinctively made a buttonhook turn and fleeing for her life slammed into her poor Doron, knocking him to the ground and sending the treasured trays of halal drumsticks sailing into the air. And as she began ploughing one by one through the defensive line of friends and relatives in a bid to reach the safety of a vehicle, Zahra caught sight of her long string of tassels, tantalizingly trailing behind her.

Even a fool could see what was coming next. As Kitten took up the chase the entire platoon of visitors broke ranks, entering into an every man for himself stampede for the cars hysteria—leaving behind in its wake a battlefield of shattered bowls, buttered chicken and samosa casualties strewn down the walkway.

Around the vehicles, chaos turned to anarchy, as the men struggled desperately amid the pandemonium to find keys and unlock doors. Zahra sensing opportunity and advantage leapt over the row of box hedges and onto the front lawn, flanking and effectively splintering the group who now took to frantically running about the yard in every direction like a flock of buttered chickens with their heads cut off.

Undeterred by all the Bollywood bedlam, Kitten continued committedly zeroing in on Annie's tassels, still attached to a shell-shocked and stone-cold frozen Parveen — white as a ghost and now pressed up with her back to a wall.

Doron, without concern for his own life, valiantly threw himself between Kitten and his poor wife— unselfishly using his little body as a human shield, desperately shooing and fanning at Zahra, while inadvertently giving Diane and me an opportunity to, with stealth, stalk up behind her.

Just as Kitten's capture seemed imminently possible, a hero bunkered down behind a car, fearing the worst was yet to come, tossed Doron an opened pink pagoda umbrella—believing it might buffer them from the evil little kitten, who, in all honesty, just wanted to play with Annie's tassels.

In any case, had our hero given it a moment's thought or consideration, perhaps arming Doron with a tassel-rimmed pink parasol might in hindsight, not have been the best of ideas.

Because as sure as eggs is eggs and faster than you could say "*Gandhi-Ji*," Zahra was lurching at the spinning wheel of fringe and fortune—reigniting a shrill-laden chorus of screams and causing one panic-stricken little brown man to begin rapidly opening and closing his parasol at Zahra, hoping to frighten her away. In fact, so expeditiously did he do this, that had he pointed it up towards the sky, I would have bet a small fortune that sooner or later he would have gotten himself airborne.

Boy what a colossal coliseum scene for the neighbours this must have been. Looking down upon the spectacle and bearing witness to the carnage of uneaten pakoras, tandoori chicken and curry-soaked goat slung about and dripping off my beloved box hedges.

Despite all the madness, once Diane had finally gotten hold of our little troublemaker and tucked her securely away in the recesses of a spare room, we all ended up having a surprisingly good laugh about the whole thing.

After the restoration of lawn and gardens and now lacking lunch, we decided to move our meeting to the Maharishi Restaurant in town, where I can happily report that not long after that, Doron and Annie not only became our business partners but good friends as well.

Dirty Deeds

Soundly suffering as I do from white coat syndrome, and as such always having tried to avoid hospitals or the doctor's office at all costs, I found myself one morning early that September reluctantly heading out to visit Dr. Lowe—in order to renew and re-validate my precious pilot's license medical requirement. A pleasant and jocular gentleman, from an era of folks that still took the time to talk and get to know their patients, he and his team nevertheless always made good the expedition.

"Ok Martin, how about the next line?" —he would query and quiz me with a subtle smile as I strenuously strained, blinked, winked, and winced my way down the eye chart. Clearly sensing that he was taking a degree of enjoyment at my distress to pass the test without the need of spectacles, I levered back,

"You know Doctor Lowe, I can even read the last line of this Snellen chart!"

"Really?"

"Yes, it says, Acme Eye Test Chart, printed by the United States Printing Office, Patent Number 707312."

Getting the gag without even a pause he bounded right back, "That's pretty good there Wile E. Coyote, ok let's check your blood pressure."

Having passed thus far, with flying colours the rudiments of the exam, he then referred me to his nurse for further consultation.

A personal and professional person, and at which point having taken a moment to review my medical history, firmly established, "Hmm... you know Martin, you are fifty-one years old and I really think you should have a blood test."

"For what?" I nervously returned.

"Nothing in particular, but let's just run a full spectrum to make sure all your levels are good."

Feeling my blood pressure rising I asked, "Is that really necessary? I mean I feel fine!"

"Yes, I think it is Martin!"

Evidently not willing to take no for an answer, I felt I had little choice if I did not want to complicate my endorsement and so headed forthwith over to the lab to provide them with a sample.

Expecting that at worst my liver had seen a little too much action over the years, I can frankly and affirmatively state that I was instead nearly bowled right back and over when Dr. Lowe phoned the following morning.

"Martin, I'm quite concerned about your P.S.A. levels. I have set up an appointment for you at the Royal Victoria Hospital to see a urologist straight away."

Now let me just say, if you are a hard-nosed and hardline hypochondriac like me, a blast of unexpected news like that can get your knees and boots shaking right down to your core.

My dear Diane, sensing that I was quickly coming apart at the seams, began immediately researching non-nefarious causes for an increase in prostate proteins.

"Hun, don't panic! Look, it says here it could be something as simple as urinary tract infection that can cause these results!"

Right, don't panic, telling a prostrated-prostate-neurotic not to panic is like telling water not to get wet!

How ironically fitting was it then that all I could see and think of at that very moment was Mathew's smugly smiling face, relishing up a plate of John Milton's revenge, that is of course, a dish best served cold.

All the same, while leaving Diane to her essential work and insisting I'd be ok going it alone, I without hesitation made the short trek up to the clinic of Dr. Iocca.

Startled to find myself suddenly surrounded in a waiting room full of significantly older men and wondering nervously what that could mean, I quickly thereafter felt the noose slowly tightening around my neck as this rather cheerful and cheery urologist called out my name.

"So Martin," offering me a seat, "let's see what's going on," while carefully reviewing my results and medical history.

"Unfortunately it appears that you do have a concerningly high level of P.S.A., especially for your age"—

triggering a kind of fear inside of me that not even standing fist to fist with the biggest bouncers in my bar-brawling days I'd ever known before.

And then, if that wasn't already taxing my nervous system, he hit me with this bomb—come over here to the examination table and drop your drawers, I'll need to stick my finger in your bum."

"WHAT THE HELL DID HE JUST SAY!?

I mean, whoa, let's just hang on a minute here, I just met you and this thing is getting way out of control.

"Look, Dr. Iocca," I tried to joke my way out of it, "not even the cops, back in my rebel-rousing days on the street had the nerve to go digging around up in there!"

Understanding of course my natural reluctance in the matter, he explained to me the importance of determining the viscidity of the gland— and with that unwavering proclamation, so came lofting down my trousers, bowing before the ultimate of ultimatums—*bend over or else fear will thee the reaper!*

At the expense of a little humiliation, I felt nonetheless relieved that we'd had a look inside, and despite the alarming lab results all seemed in good working order.

"It's a great start Martin, but I want to be sure, so I'm going to schedule you for a biopsy."

If I had thought at that very moment in my life that I now understood what was meant by invasive, I would soon discover new enlightenment on the matter only three days later, shortly after being prepped and prepared for the probe of a lifetime—more specifically a core needle biopsy, or if you prefer, the ever- kinder sounding, transrectal ultrasound!

The sheer size of this pornographically proportioned appalling apparatus was, at its very least, ungently intimidating! But to the credit of the medical staff performing the procedure, great care was taken to minimize my anxiety, pain, and discomfort. And after about an hour or so I was sent home and sternly instructed to spend the next several days quietly resting at home—to avoid, as I was once again and repeatedly warned, any unnecessary movements or strain that might cause and lead to a potentially severe infection.

At first, I took the caution of the doctors quite to heart and spent the remainder of the day resting on the sofa, while Diane cursed and nursed my tushy-trepidations. Zahra, intuitively sensing something was wrong, nuzzled and snuggled up to my side, and strangely unlike her, remained there until later that night.

By the following morning, feeling like my old self again, I insisted to Diane that I was, "Ok, I'm fine," and with Kitten afoot went stupidly about cleaning out the garage, eavestroughs and wheeling barrels of mulch about the yard and gardens—heaping, of course, onto my delicate procedure a dangerous overload of unnecessary movements and activity!

Sure enough, by the following evening I felt like death warmed over! Fever, sweating, chills, difficulty passing water and all the symptoms that made me realize I had gotten myself into a whole heap of trouble!

Diane quickly packed me up and drove me to the emergency room in Barrie, where it was soon determined that I had a raging infection and needed to be admitted forthwith!

The thought of having to stay at the hospital was so unnerving to me that I immediately began to argue the rational with the doctor suggesting maybe antibiotics at home would do the trick. Insisting on the seriousness of the situation and scaring me into co-operation with what might happen should I not take his advice, I eventually though reluctantly agreed.

Thank goodness too, because as Diane and I sat in an examination room, waiting for my room to be readied, things abruptly took a turn for the worse!

Suddenly I couldn't pass water at all, and it wasn't long before the pressure in my bladder felt as if I was going to rip open from the inside. Now heaving over in bouts of agonizing agony, Diane ran for the nurse, quickly returning together and helping me onto the bed, while making the critical determination that, "Martin, you need a catheter, I'll be right back!"

"Oh my god, I'm gonna die, Diane!" I cried out as she tried to caress and calm my ordeal.

Returning with a garden hose in her hand, the youngish nurse then warned us, "I'm sorry, I'm not too experienced with this procedure but no one else is available."

Believe you me that's not what you want to hear just before someone is about to ram and jam a conduit into your *joystick*!

And you know what? She could not have been righter!

With my manhood in one hand and the pipeline in the other, she wrangled, wrestled, pushed and shoved until I thought that surely I was soon going to pass out from either the pain or the humiliation, whichever came first!

"Maybe I need a smaller tube?" She suggested while abandoning the operation and hurriedly vacating the room.

Talk about adding insult to injury!

"Really Diane, I don't think so?!" I winced and wailed, as even in the dismal state of my distress, I man-managed to still concern myself with my ego.

"Hi Martin," the head nurse now arrived, explaining that urethral tubes often vary in diameter, as the cause and effect of the nurse's difficulties—which managed to adequately appease both her nurse and my precious ego. With that and her experience, she nevertheless quickly and precisely made the insertion, providing a relief of pain and anxiety that I beg I shall not ever know again.

Appreciatively able to afford a private room, I was quickly wheeled up and into the bed alongside a large window, with a remarkably brilliant view of the city that had a rather calming effect on my nattering nerves. This was a blessing for the same young nurse, who now needed to prepare my arm for the insertion of an intravenous drip.

Insisting that she was going to stay with me, Diane telephoned Bobby next door, and after explaining what had happened asked her to kindly feed and spend a little time with Zahra.

Responding well to the medication, by around

midnight I was feeling well enough to coax Diane out of the back-breaking chair and climb in beside me on the hospital bed for the remainder of the night.

Exhausted, we soon fell asleep.

Still spooning, as we often do, I was awoken early the following morning by a nurse whispering to the food porter as she was delivering to our room a tray of breakfast.

"I think they are still sleeping, why don't you just leave it there."

Quietly, so as not to wake Diane, I rolled over to see what was on the menu. And with all due respect to the kitchen staff of the hospital, I knew well enough that my dear Diane was going to need a Starbucks Venti English Breakfast Tea, to get her day going correctly.

Feeling surprisingly not too bad, I hush-tied the back of my gown, slipped on my slippers, repugnantly emptied my urine bag and went wheeling with my IV stand out and down to the lobby to get my spouse her fix.

"Where do think you're going?" a nurse behind the desk of the floor station suddenly accosted me.

"Um," thumbing back towards the room, "my wife didn't have a particularly good night, so I wanted to go downstairs and get her a tea."

Shocked and surely wondering who here the patient was, she eventually yet reluctantly gave me my walking papers— with the strict understanding that I come right back.

That day and the next, I was blessed with several

intermittent visits from friends and family, which gave Diane assurance that she could temporarily abandon her vigil at my bedside, bless her soul, and tend to house and home.

I also received a welcomed visit from Dr. Iocca, who, after examining my chart and my publicly paraded private parts, agreed to release me the following day— and just as importantly, have someone come shortly to remove the dreaded catheter from my demoralized loins.

Thankfully, it wasn't long before an elderly woman in hospital wear arrived at my bedside. More than grateful to finally get this gadget out of my giblets, I promptly and thoroughly tossed off my bedsheets so that she could get right down to business.

"Oh my!" obviously startled, "I'm sorry young man, I'm just here to collect your dishes."

"Yikes!"

The next morning, Diane had arrived early to collect me and my things for home when Dr. Iocca unexpectedly arrived at my room to break the bad news.

"Unfortunately, Martin, it seems you do have a small amount of cancer in the prostate."

A sobering statement that has the dramatic effect of instantly skewing one's perception of their own mortality.

"Normally," he continued to explain, while Diane caringly caressed my hand, "we would use radiation to treat the area. But given that you're just a young man I think we should remove it and be done with it. I've opened a spot on my surgery schedule the day after tomorrow, so unpack, get comfortable and I'll see you then."

I must say that the revelation of it all knocked me down pretty good—as if the skies had suddenly opened allowing for an enormous hand to come lofting down and slap my face—leaving me wreathing in agony and asking, "What was that for?" I mean, I didn't smoke or do drugs, there was little or no family history of this sort of thing, I was active, lived in the country and always ate a diverse and healthy diet—so.....what?

Eventually though, I came to believe and acknowledged the fact that conditions of the prostate affect most men to varying degrees at some point in their lives— and with that realization there was little else to do but just deal with it.

In the days leading up to my surgery, I continued to receive heartfelt visits from friends and family, that in its wake kindled within me a strange personal revelation of sorts. On my own since seventeen, I had in the years up until this very moment fought to survive, pushed ever forward, and provided for myself and my family. To become suddenly now the cared for instead of the care giver was, to say the least, a humbling experience!

Still, no matter which way I tried to skin the philosophical cat, I was, fair to say, nonetheless down in the dumps about it all. And outwardly so, everyone did their best to help smooth the road that lay ahead of me. The girls played and made me cards while Talon spent an entire night cramped in the bedside chair just to keep me company. My mother snuck in little bottles of red wine to go with my dinner and Diane arrived one evening with a furry little present concealed within an unusually large handbag.

Once the coast was sufficiently clear Zahra popped her head out of the bag and then scrambled on to the bed.

"Diane," I laughed, "we are going to get in a lot of trouble, you shouldn't have brought her."

But I had to admit, my little visitor, who took to purring and pawing at me for some time, had managed to markedly uplift my sunken spirits.

Before we could put this little nightmare to bed, so to speak, and get on with our lives, two hurdles needed clearly and correctly crossing. The first was to survive the operation and the second was to survive the recovery.

To the former, I'd have to admit that like Mathew and his irrational fears and phobias of needles, I was rearing up and flailing my hooves at the notion of being blackout-blinked into oblivion by a general anesthetic.

While most people seem to suffer slight or no concerns in the matter of forced unconsciousness, I on the other hand, was unmanly-Mathew-mushing about the room as the nurse arrived that morning to peel me away from my Diane and to deliver me post-haste to post-op.

To my surprise, I was not wheeled but instead walked, first to the waiting room, filled with fellow fallen friends and then shortly after that to the surprisingly joyful face of Dr. Iocca and his team waiting for me in the operating room.

"Hi Martin, how are you today?" he cheerfully patted and welcomed me to hop up onto the operating table. Then, turning me gently onto my back and while strapping down my arms and legs to the table as if I was being readied for the last rights on death row, the anesthetist calmly announced, "Martin you're going to taste something a little strange."

Believing that for all I had been through in life, I was now going to buy it right here and now on this table, I strangely started laughing and thinking, "Oh ya, I can taste something."

Then, precisely at that very moment, a nurse tapped me on my shoulder and asked, "How are you feeling, it will take a bit for the anesthetic to completely wear off, just relax you are fine."

In the blink of an eye, five hours had passed. Incredible!

Holding back from exclaiming, *"Well, that wasn't so bad, eh?"* I was soon gurney-carted back to my room and to the waiting arms of my dear Diane.

After several days of restful recovery at the hospital, I was granted leave by the good doctor and soon after gratefully headed home for a two-week stint of managing the pain of surgery and the pain of one callously cantankerous catheter.

Held in place at the end of the tube by an inflated ball in your bladder, I can tell you without reservation that any accidental *mishandlement* of the collection bag or perhaps some other incidental tug at the other end of the line, would provide for the wearer a new experience in the domain of pain.

Needless to say, I tried to move around as little as possible and therefore was bedridden for most of a fortnight. Thankfully, Kitten took it upon herself to spend as much time with me as she possibly could. Regularly self-bedded down at my side, scarfing back sweets and devouring delicious treats, we'd work our way through one ridiculous game show and soap opera after another.

Just in time to salvage what was left of September, I'd finally had my gear removed and was slowly getting back to my old ways— which couldn't have come any sooner for Zahra who was more than anxious to get back to our regular walks down to the pond.

Well, one fatefully terrible morning not long after that, Diane and I had decided to get ourselves ready and take Zahra out for one of our favourite walks through the back of the woods. Kitten, who was understandably anxiously and impatiently pawing at the doorway, started meowing as Diane struggled to help me tie up my boots.

"Just let her out Diane, we'll be just behind!"

Worst mistake I've ever made!

Only minutes later we exited the house and headed for the hollow while calling out for Kitten.

And just like that, she just wasn't there!

Starting to worry, we split up and began circling the house and grounds desperately yelling out for her—still nothing. Minutes soon turned into hours, as by then we had enlisted our neighbours and several friends to help and join in the search for her.

"I don't understand Bobby, she was out here alone for

five minutes, what could have happened?" Entirely beside myself, I pleaded with my friend for some plausible explanation!

"A few days ago, we had an owl here that was actually strafing down on our pup in the yard, sorry Martin might have been that."

Yet despite all the ever-growing speculations that a coyote owl or hawk was the culprit in this sordid ordeal, I on the other hand simply refused to believe it!

Surely, we'd have heard some commotion or ruckus from the open doorway—not to mention that there wasn't a trace of fur or feathers anywhere to be found.

Given that Zahra hardly ever wandered far without either of us with her, there was just no way I was going to buy into the presumption that a predator had gotten her. Furious in the extreme, I began having little doubts and soon found myself subscribing instead to the notion that she had been taken!

Abducted!

As weeks passed by without a single call on our posts and posters, Diane and I became inconsolably disheartened— eventually having to admit to ourselves that there was not going to be a happy ending here.

As we searched endlessly for some meaning to arise out of all of this heartsick mournfulness, all we could do was take some solace in the understanding that she was at very least an embodiment of the kinds of kindred spirits that in our lives we had always attracted—*and perhaps some solace in the thought that she might live on in the hearts, minds and souls of those that read about her.*

Yet still, having said all of this, I asked myself, could this, could this really be the end of her story?

To be continued . . .

About The Author

Diane and I still live near Collingwood, in Ontario, Canada, and fortunately continue to suffer from Crazy-Life Syndrome. I am looking forward to telling you more of the story in the next installment of The Culprit II.

See you soon!

Zahra